SOUND & ARTICULATION ACTIVITIES FOR CHILDREN WITH SPEECH-LANGUAGE PROBLEMS

Elizabeth Krepelin

Illustration by Bonnie Mae Smith

THE CENTER FOR APPLIED
RESEARCH IN EDUCATION
West Nyack, New York 10995

Library of Congress Cataloging-in-Publication Data

Krepelin, Elizabeth
    Sound & articulation activities for children with speech-language problems /
Elizabeth Krepelin ; illustrations by Bonnie Mae Smith.
      p.   cm.
    ISBN 0–87628–128–5 (paper)
    1. Speech therapy for children—Problems, exercises, etc. I. Title.
RJ496.S7K74   1996
818.92`85506—dc20   96–12782
                                                 CIP

Printed in the United States of America

10 9 8 7 6 5 4 3 2

ISBN 0-87628-128-5

ATTENTION: CORPORATIONS AND SCHOOLS

The Center for Applied Research in Education books are available at quantity
discounts with bulk purchase for educational, business, or sales promotional
use. For information, please write to: Prentice Hall Career & Personal
Development Special Sales, 113 Sylvan Avenue, Englewood Cliffs, NJ 07632.
Please supply: title of book, ISBN number, quantity, how the book will be used,
date needed.

**THE CENTER FOR APPLIED RESEARCH
IN EDUCATION**
West Nyack, NY 10994
A Simon & Schuster Company

On the World Wide Web at http://www.phdirect.com

Prentice Hall International (UK) Limited, *London*
Prentice Hall of Australia Pty. Limited, *Sydney*
Prentice Hall Canada, Inc., *Toronto*
Prentice Hall Hispanoamericana, S.A., *Mexico*
Prentice Hall of India Private Limited, *New Delhi*
Prentice Hall of Japan, Inc., *Tokyo*
Simon & Schuster Asia Pte. Ltd., *Singapore*
Editora Prentice Hall do Brasil, Ltda., *Rio de Janeiro*

ABOUT THE AUTHOR

ELIZABETH KREPELIN earned her B.A. and elementary teaching credentials at San Diego State College. She has twenty years of teaching experience in preschool through grade three. Mrs. Krepelin is employed by Fallbrook Union Elementary School District and is currently teaching second grade at Mary Fay Pendleton School on Camp Pendleton, a Marine base.

ABOUT THE ILLUSTRATOR

BONNIE MAE SMITH studied art in her native Boston and in San Diego. She received her B.A. and teaching credential from National University. She has taught ESL to kindergarten through fifth grade students. She is married and has three children.

Also by this author and illustrator

Ready-to-Use Flannel Board Stories, Figures and Activities for ESL Children (The Center for Applied Research in Education, 1995)

ACKNOWLEDGEMENT

Thank you to Sheryl Marvel, speech therapist at Mary Fay Pendleton School. Sheryl has generously given of her time, expertise, and encouragement.

ABOUT THIS BOOK

Sound & Articulation Activities for Children with Speech-Language Problems, a resource book for speech therapists, is designed to enrich language while improving articulation. The format can be adapted to meet the needs of speech students from preschool to grade 3.

Each section presents opportunities to practice sounds in context. The flannel board stories, puppets, and worksheets make this a versatile and fun therapy tool for young children. Early childhood teachers, special education teachers, and remedial reading teachers will also find this book helpful for teaching sound/symbol association.

Each section follows the same format:

* The ***flannel board story*** provides auditory stimulation with visual cues and combines language therapy with phonology therapy. The story vocabulary is rich with the sound being stressed, a form of intensive listening. The story and figures allow the student to manipulate the characters and review sounds. *Black-and-white* line illustrations of all flannel board figures are given at the end of each particular section. These can be used as follow-up activities, as homework, or in any other ways you wish. The *full-color* flannel board figures, found at the end of the book, need only the rough side of Velcro affixed to the back to make them ready to use.

* The ***vocabulary/intensive listening practice lists*** feature one- and two-syllable word lists for each sound. Fifteen underlined words make up the intensive listening list used for home practice. The child listens to the words being read to him or her, providing another form of auditory stimulation.

* ***Puppets,*** whose names emphasize the featured sounds, are in each section. The puppet is the main character in the flannel board story. You call the puppet by its full name; the children use the underlined portion of the name. For example, <u>Stan</u> Stegosaurus is called "Stan" by the children. All puppets come with patterns and complete step-by-step directions for assembling. Teacher-made puppets may be laminated and used repeatedly as you introduce the sound and vocabulary while the child listens. The child may make his or her own puppet to use at school and to take home with homework to practice vocabulary with parents.

* The ***parent memo*** consists of suggested vocabulary for listening practice and production practice at home. Space is allowed for you to individualize homework at your discretion. The homework format encourages therapist/parent communication.

* ***Suggested song titles and literature*** are appropriate for use with students in class and/or for home use. They feature sounds being practiced in either the lyrics or title and further reinforce the sounds.

* The ***activity pages*** consist of simple coloring, mazes, and hidden pictures for class use. These allow you time to work with individual students while others are still on task. These worksheets are appropriate homework, too.

You and your youngsters will have great fun making and using your own puppets while also improving articulation. Remember, these puppets and activities can be used in a variety of ways, so feel free to use your—and your students'—imaginations!

Elizabeth Krepelin
Bonnie Mae Smith

CONTENTS

About This Book v

Note: Each section contains a flannel board story with full-color figures and black-and-white line illustrations, vocabulary/intensive listening practice lists, puppets, parent letters, suggested songs and literature, and activity pages.

Initial Single Consonant Beginning Sounds

Bossy Belle /b/ 3

Dave Duck /d/ 10

Fat Phil /f/ 18

Gus Ghost /g/ 26

Kate Cow /k/ 34

Lew Lovebird /l/ 41

Pat Penguin /p/ 49

Rose Rat /r/ 57

Sid Seal /s/ 65

Tim Tiger /t/ 73

Final Single Consonant Sounds

Bab Crab /b/ 83

Speck Neck /k/ 90

Sad Ted /d/ 97

Tig Pig /g/ 104

Sal Camel /l/ 112

Sam Lamb /m/ 119

Ken Lion /n/ 126

Bebop Ape /p/ 133

Grr Vampire /r/ 143

Cute Cat /t/ 151

Initial Digraphs and Blends

Blue Bloodhound /bl/ 161

Chubbs Chicken /ch/ 168

Cleo Clown /kl/ 175

Crazy Crow /kr/ 183

Dru Dragon /dr/ 191

Flit Flamingo /fl/ 199

Freaky Frank /fr/ 208

Glow Worm /gl/ 215

Grumpy Gram /gr/ 222

Plaid Platypus /pl/ 230

Prisoner Prince /pr/ 238

Sherman Shark /sh/ 245

Skip Scarecrow /sk/ 254

Slow Sloane /sl/ 263

Smell Small /sm/ 270

Snow Man /sn/ 279

Speedy Spot /sp/ 286

Stan Stegosaurus /st/ 294

Swamp Swimmer /sw/ 301

Theo Thoroughbred /th/ 309

Troy Triceratops /tr/ 316

Final Combined Sounds

Swish Fish /sh/ 327

Blanche Ostrich /ch/ 334

Color Tops (colors) /ps/ 343

Building Blocks (shapes) /cks/ 347

Happy Hats (occupations) /ts/ 351

INITIAL SINGLE CONSONANT BEGINNING SOUNDS

BOSSY BELLE

FLANNEL BOARD STORY

Bossy Belle is a koala who loves to boss all the other beasts. *(figure 1)* From high in her eucalyptus tree, she bosses the birds about how to build their nests and take care of their babies. Belle even tells them when to take a bath! Belle bosses the bees in their beehives about the best way to buzz and make honey. *(figure 2)* Boy! Belle babbles by day and by night. She barks at the bear and bugs the boa. But do the beasts do her bidding? No! They go about their basic business and barely listen to busybody Bossy Belle.

BOSSY BELLE SONG

(Can be sung to "My Bonnie Lies Over the Ocean")

Bossy Belle is a born busy body.
She bosses the bird and the bee.
She bosses the bear and the boa.
She even has tried to boss me!

Bye Belle, bye Belle,
Leave me alone, let me be, be, be.
Bye Belle, bye Belle,
Leave me alone, let me be!

VOCABULARY

Initial /b/

ONE-SYLLABLE WORDS

back	barn	bee	boom	bug
bad	bath	beef	box	build
bag	beak	beet	boo	bulb
bake	beam	bib		bunk
bald	bean	bike	boss	burr
ball	bear	bird	both	burst
band	beard	birth	box	bus
hang	beast	bite	boy	buy
bank	beat	bolt	bud	buzz
bark	bed	bone		

Two-syllable words

babble	balloon	basic	beehive	boohoo
baby	bamboo	basket	before	borrow
backfire	bandage	battle	began	<u>bubble</u>
bacon	barber	beaver	boa	bucket
balance	barrel	bedroom	bonus	busy

BOSSY BELLE PUPPET

Materials:

gray construction paper;

black marker;

white, brown, and gray crayons or oil pastels;

lunch bag;

scissors;

glue

Directions:

1. Duplicate the patterns on construction paper. Cut off two inches from the bottom of the bag.

2. Trace entire figure with black marker. Color in claws and nose with black marker. Color inside of mouth black (but not bottom lip). Color eyes dark brown. Outline with black and color in black dot for pupils of eyes. Make zigzag layers of brown, gray, and white crayon around outer edges of ears to create fuzzy effect.

3. Cut out head and body. Glue on body. Line up flat edge to top crease on inner part of bottom of bag. Line up bottom flat edge to the flap of the top part of the bag, matching the line of the top part of the head to the bottom portion of the puppet.

PARENT MEMO

Today's date: _____

Child's name: _____

Dear Parent:

Please set aside five minutes a day to work on these exercises for initial /b/.

Please read these words to your child every day. Your child is to listen, but not repeat them to you.

bake	bank	beak	bike	bubble
bald	barn	beard	bolt	bush
ball	bath	beast	boo	buzz

Your child should practice saying these each day. Check off each time he or she says the words to you.

bear
0 0 0 0 0

bee
0 0 0 0 0

bird
0 0 0 0 0

box
0 0 0 0 0

bug
0 0 0 0 0

bus
0 0 0 0 0

Helping your child with speech homework will be an important advantage for your child's progress. If your child experiences difficulty or frustration, stop. Try to make your sessions brief and positive. If you want to further enrich your child's speech program and language development, you might consider checking out any of the following books from the library and reading them with your child. They contain initial /b/ in the titles.

"Baa Baa Black Sheep," Mother Goose
Barn Dance! by Bill Martin, Jr. and John Archambault
Bootsie Barker Bites by Barbara Bottner
"Little Boy Blue," Mother Goose
On the Day You Were Born by Debra Frasier
The Amazing Bone by William Steig
The Day Jimmy's Boa Ate the Wash by Trinka H. Noble

Songs you can sing emphasizing initial /b/ are "Billy Boy," "Wheels on the Bus," "The Bear Went Over the Mountain" and "My Bonnie Lies Over the Ocean."

Thank you for your support. Please sign and return this when you have completed the above lessons.

Additional Teacher Comment *(optional):*

Parent signature_____

Please write your comments, if any, on the other side of this memo.

BOSSY BELLE ACTIVITY PAGE

Color the objects that begin with /b/.

BOSSY BELLE PUPPET PATTERN

BOSSY BELLE PUPPET PATTERN

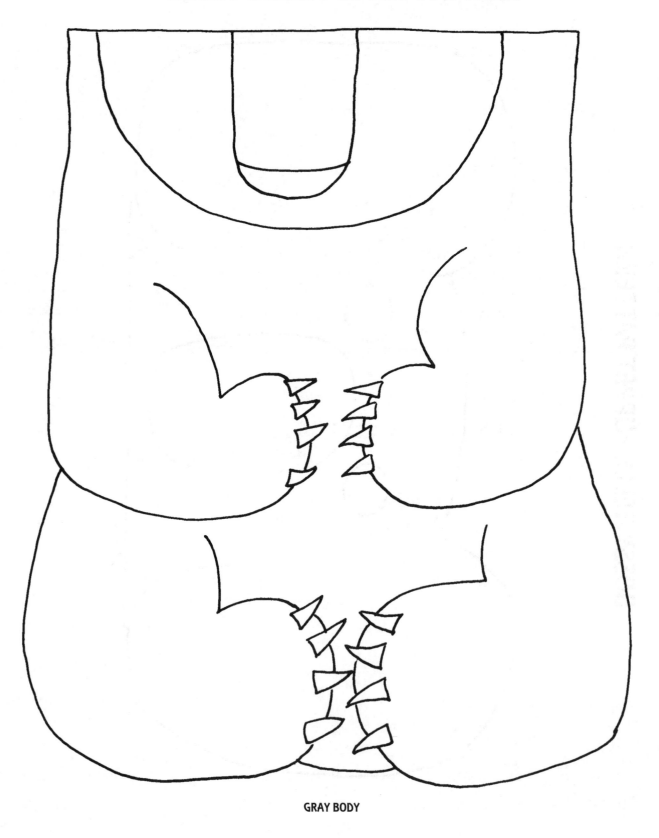

GRAY BODY

BOSSY BELLE B&W FLANNEL BOARD FIGURES

2

1

DAVE DUCK

FLANNEL BOARD STORY

Dave Duck's delight by day is to dive and dunk by the dock in Denver. *(figure 4)* Before dark, Dave dines with his date, Dinah Duck. He is a dude! He picks her up daily at dusk. They do dinner and dessert, then dance until dawn at the Duck Diner and Disco. *(figure 3)*

DAVE DUCK SONG

(Can be sung to "The Wheels on the Bus")

Dave Duck dunks and dives,
Dunks and dives, dunks and dives.
Dave Duck dunks and dives all day long.

Dinah and Dave dine and dance,
Dine and dance, dine and dance.
Dinah and Dave dine and dance from dusk 'til dawn.

VOCABULARY

Initial /d/

ONE-SYLLABLE WORDS

dad	deaf	dig	does	due
damp	<u>deck</u>	dime	dog	dug
<u>dance</u>	deed	dip	doll	<u>dull</u>
<u>dare</u>	<u>deep</u>	<u>dirt</u>	door	dump
dark	den	<u>dish</u>	<u>doubt</u>	<u>dunk</u>
dart	<u>dent</u>	dive	duck	dusk
date	<u>desk</u>	<u>dock</u>	<u>dude</u>	dust
day	dice			

TWO-SYLLABLE WORDS

daily	daughter	denim	dinner	donkey
dainty	decay	dentist	divide	<u>doughnut</u>
dairy	decide	<u>dessert</u>	dizzy	dusty
daisy	delight	devil	dollar	duty
dandy	deluxe	diet		

DAVE DUCK PUPPET

Materials:

white construction paper;

green, brown, and black marking pens or crayons;

lunch bag;

scissors;

glue

Directions:

1. Duplicate the patterns on construction paper. Cut off one inch from the bottom of the bag.

2. Dave is a mallard duck. Color head to the neck line green. The rest of the body of the duck is colored brown. Draw on eyes and trace lines with black. Color inside of mouth solid black.

3. Cut out all pieces. Glue on bottom part of duck. Glue on head, lining up flat edge with bottom of flap of bag. Glue on bottom of beak, lining up to center of the bag. Glue on top of beak, being careful not to get glue on the bottom (wider portion) of beak, which hangs down. (This would glue together the mouth.) Glue on feet.

PARENT MEMO

Today's date: _____

Child's name: _____

Dear Parents:

Please set aside five minutes a day to work on these exercises for initial /d/.

Please read these words to your child every day. Your child is to listen, but not repeat them to you.

dance	deep	dessert	dock	dude
dare	dent	dirt	doubt	dull
deck	desk	dish	doughnut	dunk

Your child should practice saying these each day. Check off each time he or she says the words to you.

dart
0 0 0 0 0

dice
0 0 0 0 0

dog
0 0 0 0 0

doll
0 0 0 0 0

door
0 0 0 0 0

duck
0 0 0 0 0

Helping your child with speech homework will be an important advantage for your child's progress. If your child experiences difficulty or frustration, stop. Try to make your sessions brief and positive. If you want to further enrich your child's speech program and language development, you might consider checking out any of the following books from the library and reading them with your child. They contain initial /d/ in the titles.

Deep in the Forest by Brinton Turkle
Go, Dog, Go by Philip D. Eastman
"Hickory Dickory Dock," Mother Goose
"Hey Diddle Diddle," Mother Goose
If the Dinosaurs Came Back by Bernard Most
Patrick's Dinosaurs by Carol Carrick
101 Dalmations by Walt Disney Staff
Ten Black Dots by Donald Crews

A song you can sing emphasizing initial /d/ is "The Farmer in the Dell."

Thank you for your support. Please sign and return this when you have completed the above lessons.

Additional Teacher Comment *(optional):*

Parent signature_____

Please write your comments, if any, on the other side of this memo.

DAVE DUCK ACTIVITY PAGE

Circle the pictures that begin with /d/.

13

DAVE DUCK PUPPET PATTERN

GREEN HEAD

14

WHITE NECK, BROWN BODY

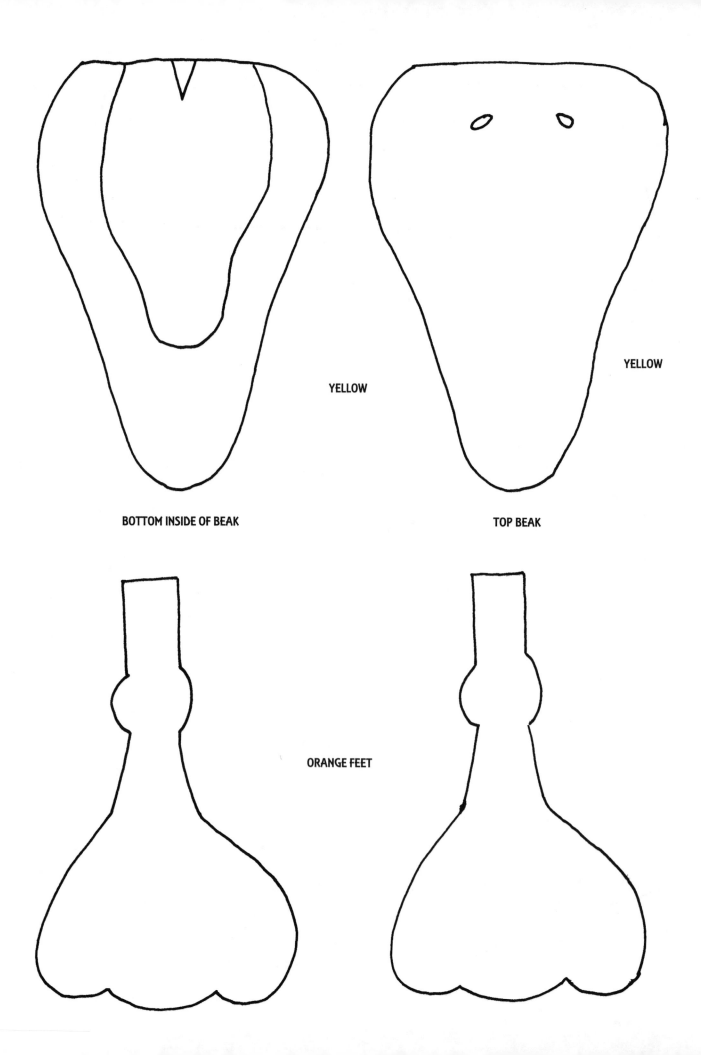

YELLOW

YELLOW

BOTTOM INSIDE OF BEAK

TOP BEAK

ORANGE FEET

DAVE DUCK B&W FLANNEL BOARD FIGURES

FAT PHIL

FLANNEL BOARD STORY

Please don't fuss or feel sad for Fat Phil. *(figure 5)* He is fat because his favorite thing is to feed his face. He feasts on fine food like fish and fudge. *(figure 6)* He never uses a fork—he says all food is finger food! He eats fast, but he never gets full! Phil is so fat, he is fast becoming famous. He's first to start and last to finish. Fortunately, fat is fashionable when you are a hippopotamus like Phil!

FAT PHIL SONG

(Can be sung to "The Bear Went Over the Mountain")

Phil feasts on fudge
Phil feasts on fudge
Phil feasts on fudge
Until he gets his fill
Until he gets his fill
Until he gets his fill
Phil feasts on fudge until he gets his fill
As if he ever will
As if he ever will
Phil feasts on fudge until he gets his fill.

VOCABULARY

Initial /f/

ONE-SYLLABLE WORDS

face	fang	fierce	fix	four
fact	far	fight	fizz	fudge
fade	farm	film	fog	full
fall	fast	fin	fold	fun
faint	fat	find	food	fuss
fair	fear	fire	fool	fuzz
faith	feast	first	fork	Phil
fall	feel	fish	fort	phone
fan	feet	five	found	

TWO-SYLLABLE WORDS

fable	fasten	feline	<u>firefly</u>	footprint
<u>fairy</u>	father	fever	fireman	forget
famous	faucet	fiddle	fizzle	forgive
<u>fancy</u>	favor	finger	follow	forward
farmer	<u>feather</u>	finish	football	funny

FAT PHIL PUPPET

Materials:

light gray construction paper;

hot pink or any other light colored, bright construction paper;

yellow, pink, and black markers or crayons;

lunch bag;

scissors;

glue

Directions:

1. Duplicate the patterns on construction paper. Cut off one inch from the bottom of the bag.

2. Outline hippo head and body with black. Fill in nostrils and draw on eyes. Color inside of mouth pink. Color teeth and nails yellow. Color letters for "Feed Me" with bright, dark contrasting color.

3. Cut out all parts. Glue bottom part of body to bottom part of bag, lining flat part to crease. Glue on head, lining up to lines of chin. Glue bib on so it looks like it fits on neck.

PARENT MEMO

Today's date: _____

Child's name: _____

Dear Parent:

Please set aside five minutes a day to work on these exercises for initial /f/.

Please read these words to your child every day. Your child is to listen, but not repeat them to you.

fancy	farm	feast	fierce	firefly
faith	fast	feather	fight	fudge
fairy	fat	feel	fin	fun

Your child should practice saying these each day. Check off each time he or she says the words to you.

fan
0 0 0 0 0

fish
0 0 0 0 0

fire
0 0 0 0 0

fork
0 0 0 0 0

phone
0 0 0 0 0

four
0 0 0 0 0

Helping your child with speech homework will be an important advantage for your child's progress. If your child experiences difficulty or frustration, stop. Try to make your sessions brief and positive. If you want to further enrich your child's speech program and language development, you might consider checking out any of the following books from the library and reading them with your child. They contain initial /f/ in the titles.

Five Chinese Brothers by Claire H. Bishop
Fox All Week by Edward Marshall
Going to Sleep on the Farm by Wendy C. Lewison
One Fish, Two Fish, Red Fish, Blue Fish by Dr. Seuss
Our Animal Friends at Maple Hill Farm by Alice and Martin Provensen
The Foot Book by Dr. Seuss

Songs you can sing emphasizing initial /f/ are "Old MacDonald Had a Farm" and "The Farmer in the Dell."

Thank you for your support. Please sign and return this when you have completed the above lessons.

Additional Teacher Comment (*optional*):

Parent signature _____

Please write your comments, if any, on the other side of this memo.

FAT PHIL ACTIVITY PAGE

FEED ME!

Call Jake
444-0440
bread + Milk

Color the pictures that begin with /f/.

21

FAT PHIL PUPPET PATTERN

FAT PHIL PUPPET PATTERN

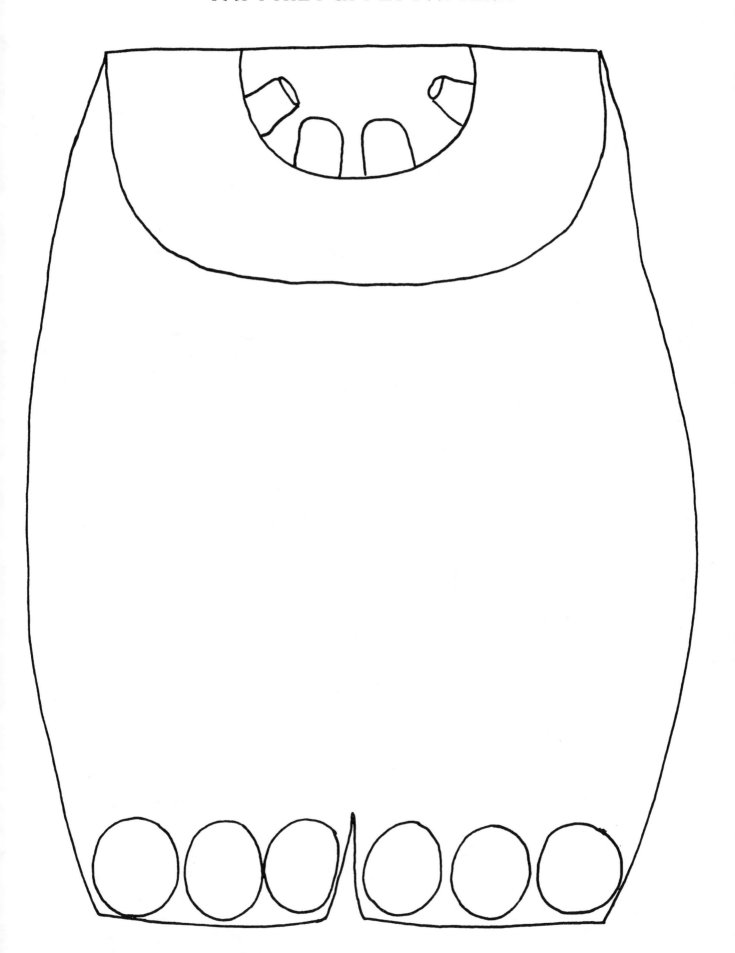

FAT PHIL PUPPET PATTERN

FAT PHIL B&W FLANNEL BOARD FIGURES

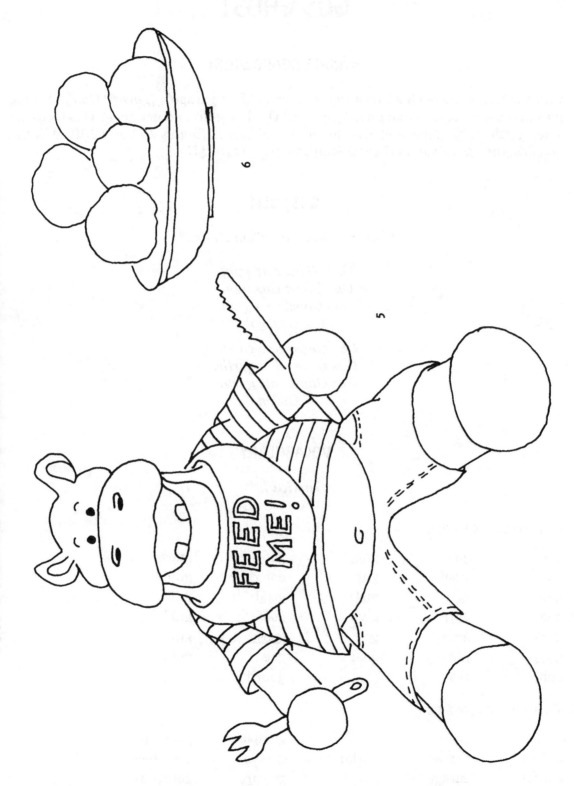

GUS GHOST

FLANNEL BOARD STORY

Can you guess where Gus Ghost *(figure 7)* lives? In a garage! *(figure 8)* Goofy Gus giggles and gasps at girls and guys. *(figure 9)* Do they gulp and get gone? Goodness, no! They giggle at his game and give him gum and garlic. *(figures 10A and 10B)* When he gobbles, they get away in their golden go-cart. *(figure 11)*

GUS POEM

(Can be sung to "'Dem Bones")

Gus Ghost eats gum.
Gus Ghost eats gum.
Gus Ghost eats gum.
Go, Gus, go!

Gus Ghost eats garlic.
Gus Ghost eats garlic.
Gus Ghost eats garlic.
Go, Gus, go!

VOCABULARY

Initial /g/

ONE-SYLLABLE WORDS

gab	<u>gas</u>	<u>ghost</u>	gone	guess
gage	gasp	<u>gift</u>	gong	guide
gain	<u>gate</u>	<u>girl</u>	<u>good</u>	guilt
gale	<u>gave</u>	give	goof	gulf
<u>game</u>	gaze	<u>go</u>	<u>goose</u>	gull
<u>gang</u>	geese	goal	got	gulp
gap	get	<u>goat</u>	guard	gum

TWO-SYLLABLE WORDS

gadget	galore	Garfield	goalpost	<u>goldfish</u>
gallant	gander	garland	gobble	good-bye
gallon	garage	garlic	<u>go-cart</u>	gorgeous
gallop	garden	ghastly	golden	<u>gumdrop</u>

GUS GHOST PUPPET

Materials:

white construction paper;

black crayon or marker;

lunch bag;

scissors;

glue

Directions:

1. Duplicate the patterns on construction paper. Cut off one inch from the bottom of the bag.

2. Outline the entire figure with black crayon or marking pen. Fill in the mouth with black. Add eyes and nose. Cut out all pieces. Glue top of head to the paper bag, lining up the edge with the edge of the top flap. Glue on the bottom part, lining up the top edge with the crease in the bag. Be sure to line up the mouth.

PARENT MEMO

Today's date: _____

Child's name: _____

Dear Parent:

Please set aside five minutes a day to work on these exercises for initial /g/.

Please read these words to your child every day. Your child is to listen, but not repeat them to you.

game	gate	gift	goat	go-cart
gang	gave	girl	good	goldfish
gas	ghost	go	goose	gumdrop

Your child should practice saying these each day. Check off each time he or she says the words to you.

game
0 0 0 0 0

gas
0 0 0 0 0

gate
0 0 0 0 0

goat
0 0 0 0 0

goose
0 0 0 0 0

gum
0 0 0 0 0

Helping your child with speech homework will be an important advantage for your child's progress. If your child experiences difficulty or frustration, stop. Try to make your sessions brief and positive. If you want to further enrich your child's speech program and language development, you might consider checking out any of the following books from the library and reading them with your child. They contain initial /g/ in the titles.

Goodnight Moon by Margaret Wise Brown
Three Billy Goats Gruff (any version)
Goldilocks and the Three Bears (any version)
Gorilla by Anthony Brown
Go, Dog, Go by Philip D. Eastman

Songs you can sing emphasizing initial /g/ are "Go Tell Aunt Rhodie" and "The Good Morning Song."

Thank you for your support. Please sign and return this when you have completed the above lessons.

Additional Teacher Comment *(optional):*

Parent signature _____

Please write your comments, if any, on the other side of this memo.

GUS GHOST ACTIVITY PAGE

Color the pictures that begin with /g/.

GUS GHOST PUPPET PATTERN

GUS GHOST PUPPET PATTERN

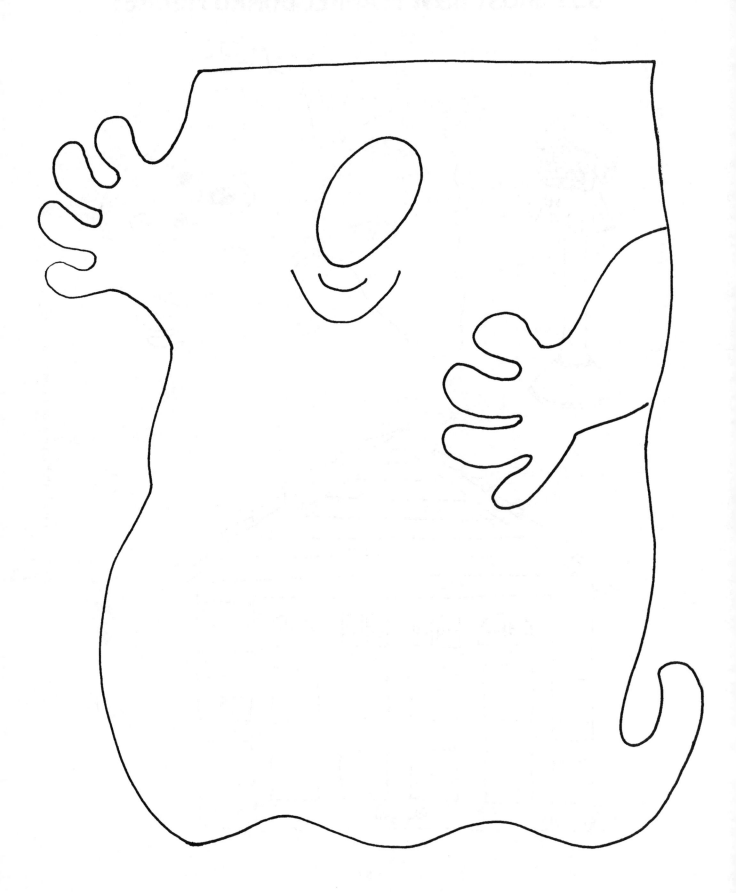

GUS GHOST B&W FLANNEL BOARD FIGURES

10A

8

GUS GHOST B&W FLANNEL BOARD FIGURES

10B

9

11

KATE COW

FLANNEL BOARD STORY

Kate Cow is cool and calm. *(figure 12)* She cares for her calf, Kermit. *(figure 13)* She keeps him clean and content. He can count on Kate to come when he calls. Kate covers Kermit with countless cow kisses. (*(figure 14)*

KATE COW POEM

(Can be sung to "This Old Man")

Kate Cow, cool and calm
Comes when Kermit calls, "Mom!"
With a moo moo, kick and chew
Help is on the way.
Kate Cow coolly saves the day.

VOCABULARY

Initial /k/

ONE-SYLLABLE WORDS

cage	cap	coast	corn	cut
cake	cape	cob	cost	keep
calf	car	coin	cough	key
call	card	cold	could	kick
calm	care	comb	count	kid
came	cart	come	cow	kind
camp	cat	cone	cub	king
can	caught	cook	cud	kiss
cane	cave	cool	curl	kite

TWO-SYLLABLE WORDS

cabbage	camel	carrot	confuse	cozy
cabin	camper	carry	contest	ketchup
caboose	candle	castle	cookie	kitchen
cackle	candy	cobweb	corner	kitten
cactus	canoe	coffee	cowboy/girl	

KATE COW PUPPET

Materials:

white construction paper;
brown and black marking pens or crayons;
lunch bag;
scissors;
glue

Directions:

1. Duplicate patterns on construction paper.
2. Trace the head and body with black crayon or marker. Color inside of mouth black. Draw black cow spots on head and body. Draw or free-cut brown eyes.
3. Cut out head and body. Glue body to bag. Glue head to bag, lining up mouth.

PARENT MEMO

Today's date: _____

Child's name: _____

Dear Parent:

Please set aside five minutes a day to work on these exercises for initial /k/.

Please read these words to your child every day. Your child is to listen, but not repeat them to you.

cage	can	carrot	cold	cow
cake	candle	cat	comb	key
camp	car	cave	corn	kite

Your child should practice saying these each day. Check off each time he or she says the words to you.

cake
0 0 0 0 0

cat
0 0 0 0 0

corn
0 0 0 0 0

cow
0 0 0 0 0

key
0 0 0 0 0

kite
0 0 0 0 0

Helping your child with speech homework will be an important advantage for your child's progress. If your child experiences difficulty or frustration, stop. Try to make your sessions brief and positive. If you want to further enrich your child's speech program and language development, you might consider checking out any of the following books from the library and reading them with your child. They contain initial /k/ in the titles.

The Very Hungry Caterpillar by Eric Carle
Millions of Cats by Wanda Gag
Caps for Sale by Esphyr Slobodkina
The Carrot Seed by Ruth Krauss
The Three Little Kittens (any version)
Old King Cole (any version)

Songs you can sing emphasizing initial /k/ are "She'll Be Comin' Round the Mountain" and "In a Cabin in the Wood."

Thank you for your support. Please sign and return this when you have completed the above lessons.

Additional Teacher Comment *(optional)*:

Parent signature _____

Please write your comments, if any, on the other side of this memo.

KATE COW ACTIVITY PAGE

Color the pictures that begin with /k/.

KATE COW PUPPET PATTERN

WHITE

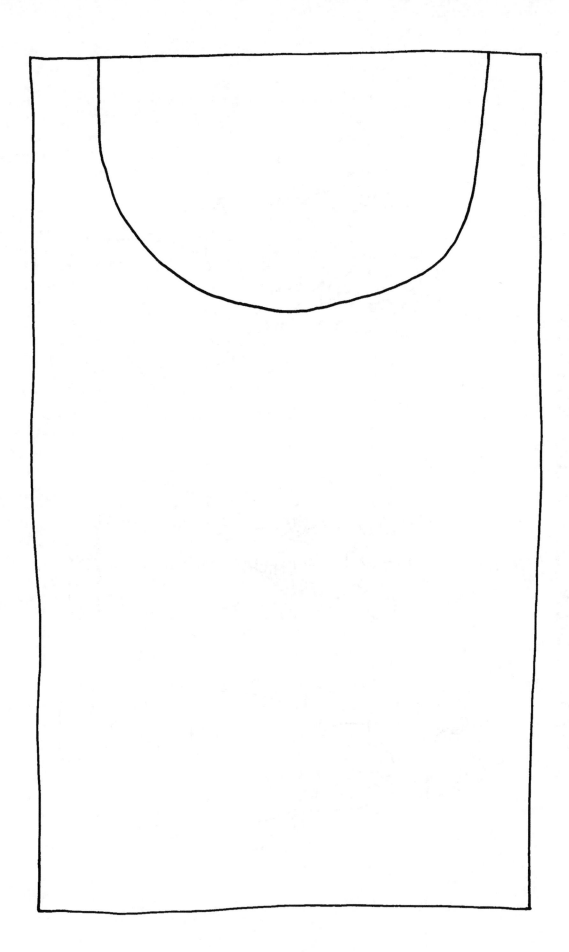

WHITE BODY

KATE COW B&W FLANNEL BOARD FIGURES

14

13

12

LEW LOVEBIRD

FLANNEL BOARD STORY

(figure 15) Lew Lovebird longed for a lady love. He looked high and low. Late one night, by the light of the moon, he at last found Lola in a lemon tree. *(figure 16)* He lost his heart to lovely Lola. With a low laugh, Lew leaped to Lola, landing lightly beside her. The loving little birds have lived on a limb located on Lover's Lane since that long ago, lucky night. *(figure 17 for birds to sit on)*

LEW LOVEBIRD POEM

(Can be sung to "Are You Sleeping?")

Lew and Lola, Lew and Lola,
Lovebirds two,
Lovebirds two.
Lucky, laughing, living,
Made for love and giving.
Lola and Lew,
Lola and Lew.

VOCABULARY

Initial /l/

ONE-SYLLABLE WORDS

lace	large	leave	lime	look
lad	late	left	line	lost
laid	laugh	leg	lip	loud
lake	law	less	list	love
lamb	lead	let	load	low
lamp	leaf	lick	loaf	luck
land	league	life	lock	lump
lane	lean	light	log	lunch
lap	learn	like	long	lung

TWO-SYLLABLE WORDS

ladder	leader	letter	lizard	lucky
lady	lemon	lightning	llama	lunchroom
lazy	lesson	listen	lovebird	

LEW OR LOLA LOVEBIRD PUPPET

Materials:

Lovebird can be any bright color you want: for example, turquoise, yellow, or chartreuse construction paper for bodies and hot pink or bright orange for feet, legs, and beak; various colored construction paper scraps; black markers; lunch bag; scissors; glue

Directions:

1. Duplicate the patterns on construction paper. Cut off three inches from the bottom of the bag. Cut 1 × 6-inch or 1 × 12-inch strips for legs. (The length will depend on whether you want a long legged Lew [or Lola] or a short legged Lew [or Lola]!)

2. Cut out all parts. Glue the head to the bag, flat side lined up with flap of bag. Glue body to bag, flat edge lined up to top crease of bag. Glue on heart-shaped beak to head. Line up bottom portion of the beak. The flat part should line up to the top of the crease. The rest should match the top part of the beak. Glue on wings. Accordion-fold two strips for legs. Attach the heart-shaped feet to the bottom of the strips (pointed side of the hearts attach to the strip). Glue legs to the back of the body. Make eyes with marker or use construction paper.

3. If desired, create a bow tie for Lew. Many details can be added to make Lew (or Lola) wild, crazy and your creation. Feathers could be painted on with contrasting paint using a folded index card.

PARENT MEMO

Today's date: _____

Child's name: _____

Dear Parent:

Please set aside five minutes a day to work on these exercises for initial /l/.

Please read these words to your child every day. Your child is to listen, but not repeat them to you.

lace	lamb	learn	lightning	love
ladder	lamp	leg	lime	luck
lake	leaf	light	lock	lunch

Your child should practice saying these each day. Check off each time he or she says the words to you.

lamb 0 0 0 0 0

lamp 0 0 0 0 0

leaf 0 0 0 0 0

lime 0 0 0 0 0

lock 0 0 0 0 0

love 0 0 0 0 0

Helping your child with speech homework will be an important advantage for your child's progress. If your child experiences difficulty or frustration, stop. Try to make your sessions brief and positive. If you want to further enrich your child's speech program and language development, you might consider checking out any of the following books from the library and reading them with your child. They contain initial /l/ in the titles.

A Kiss for Little Bear by Else H. Minarik
Angus Lost by Marjorie Flack
Little Toot by Hardie Gramatky
The Grouchy Ladybug by Eric Carle

Songs you can sing emphasizing initial /l/ are "Twinkle, Twinkle Little Star," "Lollipop," and "Mary Had a Little Lamb."

Thank you for your support. Please sign and return this when you have completed the above lessons.

Additional Teacher Comment *(optional):*

Parent signature _____

Please write your comments, if any, on the other side of this memo.

LEW OR LOLA LOVEBIRD ACTIVITY PAGE

Find pictures that begin with /l/ hidden in the tree. Color them.

©1996 by Elizabeth Krepelin and Bonnie Mae Smith

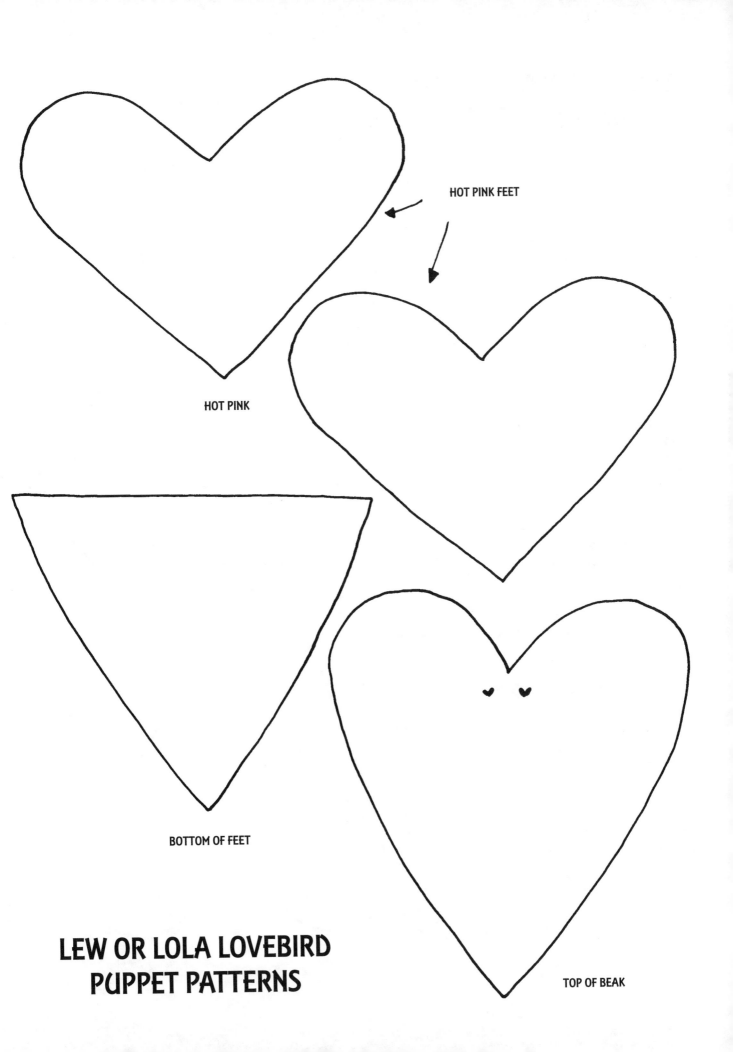

HOT PINK FEET

HOT PINK

BOTTOM OF FEET

LEW OR LOLA LOVEBIRD
PUPPET PATTERNS

TOP OF BEAK

LEW OR LOLA LOVEBIRD
PUPPET PATTERNS

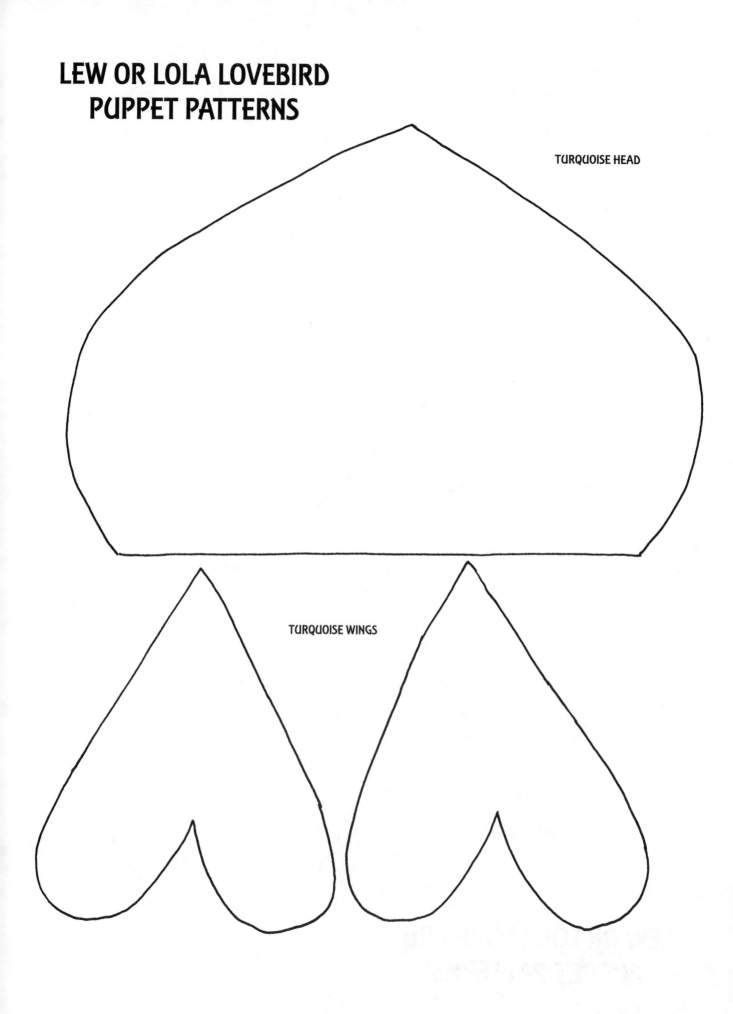

TURQUOISE HEAD

TURQUOISE WINGS

LEW OR LOLA LOVEBIRD PUPPET PATTERN

TURQUOISE BODY

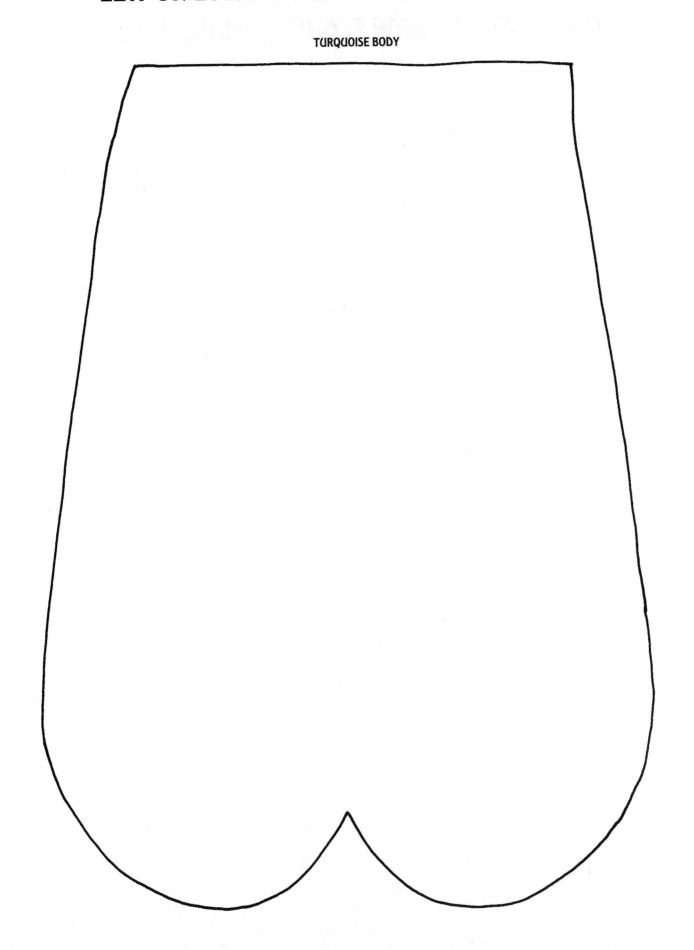

LEW LOVEBIRD B&W FLANNEL BOARD FIGURES

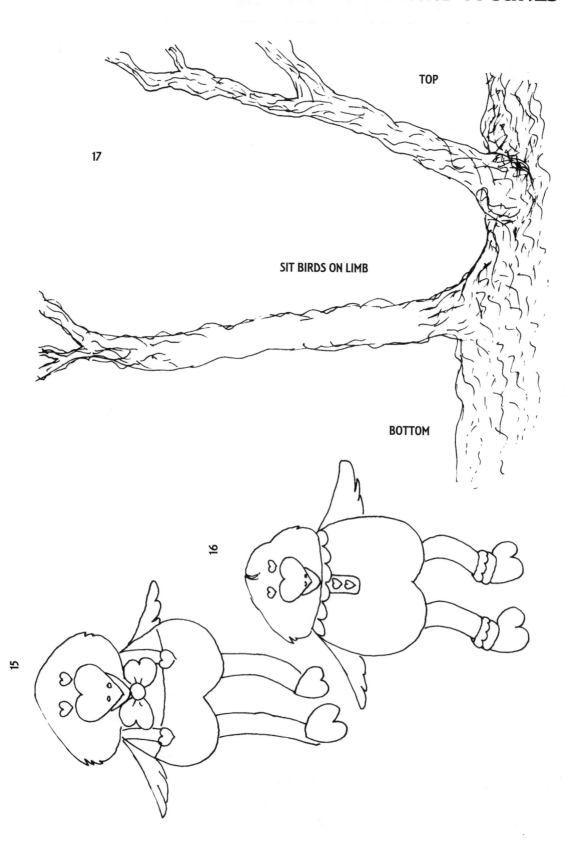

TOP

17

SIT BIRDS ON LIMB

BOTTOM

16

15

PAT PENGUIN

FLANNEL BOARD STORY

Pat Penguin loves to go on picnics with her pal, Pam. *(figure 18)* They prepare pickles, pizza, pancakes, pea soup, peach pie, pears, popcorn, pretzels, peanuts. They pack plenty of Dr. Pepper® because it is their favorite soda pop. "Perfect!" Pat says when it is all packed.

Pam and Pat paddle, panting and puffing with their picnic, to a perch in the Pole park. Piece by piece, they put that picnic into their mouths. *(figure 19)* Poor Pam and Pat. They have pain and get puffed up after that! Perhaps they will learn not to be such pigs!

PAT PENGUIN SONG

(Can be sung to "Jingle Bells")

Pat and Pam, Pat and Pam,
Perfect picnic pals.
Packed some pizza, pickles and pie,
They were hungry gals.

Pat and Pam, Pat and Pam,
Got a tummy ache.
Penguins shouldn't be such pigs
On picnics, goodness sake!

VOCABULARY

Initial /p/

ONE-SYLLABLE WORDS

pace	pant	peace	pill	<u>pout</u>
pack	<u>park</u>	<u>peach</u>	<u>pine</u>	<u>puff</u>
<u>page</u>	part	pear	pink	pull
<u>pail</u>	<u>paste</u>	<u>pearl</u>	pipe	pup
pain	pat	peek	<u>point</u>	purse
<u>paint</u>	path	peep	poke	<u>push</u>
pair	pause	pep	pond	put
pal	paw	<u>perch</u>	poor	putt
palm	pay	<u>pet</u>	pop	
pan	pea	pie	pound	

TWO-SYLLABLE WORDS

package	paper	pebble	perfect	poem	posy
paddle	parade	pedal	perfume	polish	power
palace	parent	pencil	person	popcorn	puddle
pamper	parrot	penguin	pickle	porpoise	puppet
pancake	partner	penny	pizza	porridge	purple
panda	pasture	people	pocket	possum	puzzle
panther	peanut	pepper			

PAT PENGUIN PUPPET

Materials:

white and gray construction paper;

2 gummed reinforcements per puppet;

black marking pen;

lunch bag;

scissors;

glue

Directions:

1. Duplicate the patterns on construction paper. Cut off one inch from the bottom of the bag.

2. Color the head and wings black. Outline the feet and color in the toe nails.

3. Cut out all parts. Glue on the head, lining the flat part with the edge of the bag. Glue on body, going all the way to the crease and lining up the top of the head with the bottom part. Center bottom of beak on body, putting the flat top edge even with the inside crease of the bag. Line up the top beak with the bottom. Glue the edge that is on the bag. Be careful not to get glue on the bottom edge that hangs over so you don't glue the mouth together. Glue the feet to the back of the puppet so they are peeking out from the bottom.

PARENT MEMO

Today's date: _____

Child's name: _____

Dear Parent:

Please set aside five minutes a day to work on these exercises for initial /p/.

Please read these words to your child every day. Your child is to listen, but not repeat them to you.

page	park	pearl	pickle	pout
pail	paste	perch	pine	puff
paint	peach	pet	point	push

Your child should practice saying these each day. Check off each time he or she says the words to you.

pail
0 0 0 0 0

paint
0 0 0 0 0

palm
0 0 0 0 0

peach
0 0 0 0 0

pie
0 0 0 0 0

pipe
0 0 0 0 0

Helping your child with speech homework will be an important advantage for your child's progress. If your child experiences difficulty or frustration, stop. Try to make your sessions brief and positive. If you want to further enrich your child's speech program and language development, you might consider checking out any of the following books from the library and reading them with your child. They contain initial /p/ in the titles.

Harold and the Purple Crayon by Crockett Johnson
Mouse Paint by Ellen S. Walsh
Pancake, Pancake by Eric Carle
Polar Bear, Polar Bear, What Do You Hear? by Eric Carle
"Peas Porridge Hot," Mother Goose
"Peter, Peter, Pumpkin Eater," Mother Goose
Tacky the Penguin by Helen Lester

Songs you can sing emphasizing initial /p/ are "Pop Goes the Weasel" and "Puff the Magic Dragon."

Thank you for your support. Please sign and return this when you have completed the above lessons.

Additional Teacher Comment *(optional):*

Parent signature _____

Please write your comments, if any, on the other side of this memo.

PAT PENGUIN ACTIVITY PAGE

Color the pictures that begin with /p/.

PAT PENGUIN PUPPET PATTERN

WHITE

PAT PENGUIN PUPPET PATTERNS

WHITE HEAD

UPPER

LOWER

BEAK

FEET

PAT PENGUIN B&W FLANNEL BOARD FIGURE

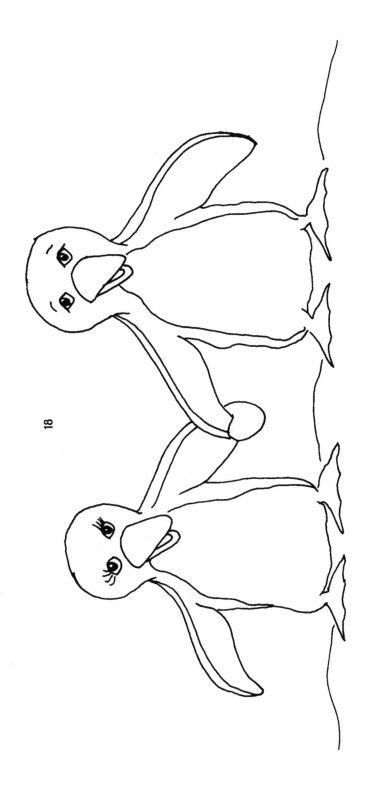

18

PAT PENGUIN B&W FLANNEL BOARD FIGURE

19

ROSE RAT

FLANNEL BOARD STORY

Have you heard of Rose Rat and the Rebels? They can really rock and roll! Rob Rabbit plays lead guitar. *(figure 20)* Rick Raccoon plays rhythm *(figure 21)* and Rachel Reptile is on drums. *(figure 22)* Rose Rat raps rhymes. *(figure 23)* They raise the roof on the room when they shake, rattle, and roll! *(figure 24)*

ROSE RAT POEM

(Can be sung to "Rock Around the Clock")

Rah, rah, Rose Rat, rattle and roll.
Rah, rah, Rose Rat, rattle and roll.
Rah, rah, Rose Rat, rattle and roll.
Rose Rat rocks all right!

When Rose Rat raps a tune
The roof gets rocked right off the room.
Rose raps a rhyme just right,
She rocks and rolls all through the night.
Rock, rock, rock,
Rose Rat rocks just right.

VOCABULARY

Initial /r/

ONE-SYLLABLE WORDS

race	rap	rich	roof	rug
rag	rat	ride	room	rule
rail	read	right	rope	run
rain	real	ring	rose	rush
raise	red	ripe	rough	rust
rake	rent	road	round	wrap
ran	rhyme	roast	row	wreath
ranch	rib	rock	rub	wrench
range	rice	roll	rude	wrong

TWO-SYLLABLE WORDS

<u>rabbit</u>	raisin	recess	rescue	rocket
<u>raccoon</u>	rascal	relax	ribbon	rodent
radish	rattle	remind	riddle	rotten
<u>rainbow</u>	ready	reptile	robin	royal

ROSE RAT PUPPET

Materials:

light gray construction paper;

markers or crayons;

lunch bag;

scissors;

stapler;

glue

Directions

1. Duplicate the patterns on construction paper.

2. In order for Rose to turn out just right you need to modify the bag a bit. Cut off four inches from the bottom of the bag. Cut off the sides of the flap of the bag at the corner, in a triangle shape. Staple edges, being careful to staple the flap and not the bottom part of the bag.

3. Trace head and body with black marker. Fill in nose and eyes with solid black. Color the earrings, microphone, and headband. You can really make her headband snazzy with bright colors, stripes, and polka dots. Use your imagination!

4. Cut out the head and body and glue the body to the bag first. Line up whisker lines to get the head on just right.

PARENT MEMO

Today's date: _____

Child's name: _____

Dear Parent:

Please set aside five minutes a day to work on these exercises for initial /r/.

Please read these words to your child every day. Your child is to listen, but not repeat them to you.

rabbit	rake	rhyme	road	rope
raccoon	ranch	rice	rock	rude
rainbow	read	right	room	wrench

Your child should practice saying these each day. Check off each time he or she says the words to you.

rain
O O O O O

rake
O O O O O

ring
O O O O O

rose
O O O O O

rug
O O O O O

wreath
O O O O O

Helping your child with speech homework will be an important advantage for your child's progress. If your child experiences difficulty or frustration, stop. Try to make your sessions brief and positive. If you want to further enrich your child's speech program and language development, you might consider checking out any of the following books from the library and reading them with your child. They contain initial /r/ in the titles.

Little Red Riding Hood (any version)
Rain Makes Applesauce by Julian Scheer
Rapunzel (any version)
Really Rosie (a video)
Rumplestiltskin (any version)
The Little Red Hen (any version)

Songs you can sing emphasizing initial /r/ are "Row, Row, Row Your Boat," "I Saw a Little Rooster," and "Go Tell Aunt Rhodie."

Thank you for your support. Please sign and return this when you have completed the above lessons.

Additional Teacher Comment *(optional):*

Parent signature _____

Please write your comments, if any, on the other side of this memo.

ROSE RAT ACTIVITY PAGE

Color the characters that begin with /r/.

ROSE RAT PUPPET PATTERN

LIGHT GRAY

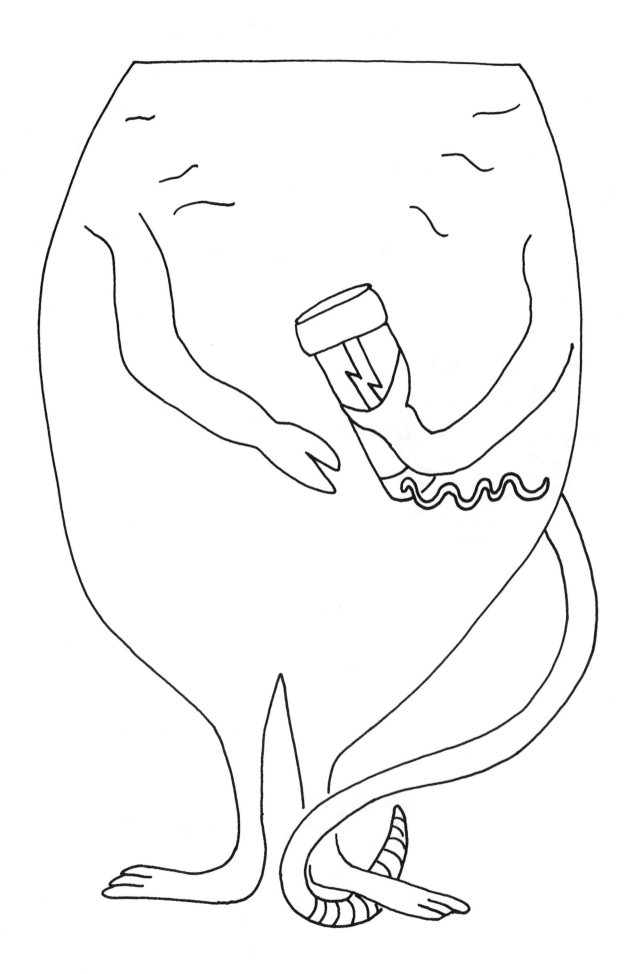

ROSE RAT B&W FLANNEL BOARD FIGURES

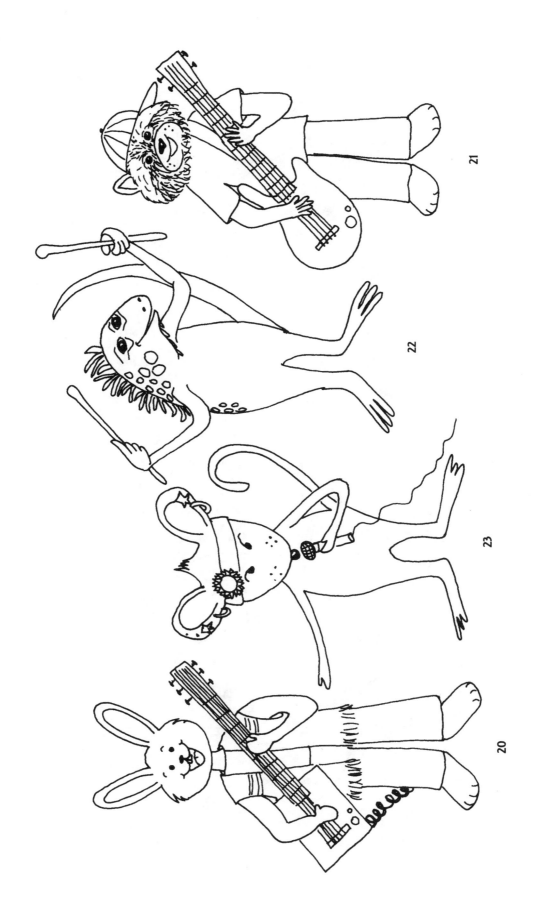

21

22

23

20

ROSE RAT B&W FLANNEL BOARD FIGURE

24

SID SEAL

FLANNEL BOARD STORY

Say! Have you seen Sid Seal? He said he'd see me soon. I hope he's safe, not sick or sad or sulking somewhere. He lives here in the sea *(figure 25)* where he likes to swim and sail in the salty surf. I've searched everywhere under the sun for him. Maybe he's searching for sunken treasure *(figure 26)* or playing hide and seek. If you see him, tell him you saw me. He's a soft, silky silver color and makes a barking sound. He's the silliest seal you ever saw. I am sorry I missed him. Well, see ya!

SID SEAL POEM

(Can be sung to "Do You Know the Muffin Man?")

Have you seen Sid Seal,
Sid Seal, Sid Seal?
Have you seen Sid Seal
Who surfs in the sea?

Yes, we've seen Sid Seal,
Sid Seal, Sid Seal.
Yes, we've seen Sid Seal
Who surfs in the sea.

VOCABULARY

Initial /s/

ONE-SYLLABLE WORDS

cent	sat	self	soap	sow
sack	save	serve	sock	such
sad	saw	sew	soft	suds
safe	say	sick	song	suit
said	sea	sign	soon	sulk
sail	seal	silk	sound	sum
saint	search	sink	soup	sun
salt	seed	sit	sour	sunk
sand	seek	size	south	surf

TWO-SYLLABLE WORDS

ceiling	city	sandwich	silent	sudden
cement	saddle	satin	silly	summer
center	sailboat	season	silver	Sunday
cider	salad	selfish	soda	sunshine
circle	sandal	seven	sorry	surprise

SID SEAL PUPPET

Materials:

light gray construction paper;

crayons;

lunch bag;

scissors;

glue

Directions:

1. Duplicate the patterns on construction paper. Cut off one inch from the bottom of the bag.

2. Outline puppet with black. Color eyes dark brown. Color teeth solid white. Color in top of mouth solid black. Color most of inside of mouth solid black; color edges by teeth pink.

3. Cut out pieces and glue to bag.

PARENT MEMO

Today's date: _____

Child's name: _____

Dear Parent:

Please set aside five minutes a day to work on these exercises for initial /s/.

Please read these words to your child every day. Your child is to listen, but not repeat them to you.

center	sand	sign	soap	sour
safe	search	silly	song	sunshine
sail	serve	size	soup	surf

Your child should practice saying these each day. Check off each time he or she says the words to you.

sad
O O O O O

salt
O O O O O

seal
O O O O O

seed
O O O O O

sock
O O O O O

sun
O O O O O

Helping your child with speech homework will be an important advantage for your child's progress. If your child experiences difficulty or frustration, stop. Try to make your sessions brief and positive. If you want to further enrich your child's speech program and language development, you might consider checking out any of the following books from the library and reading them with your child. They contain initial /s/ in the titles.

Hide and Seek in the Yellow House by Agatha Rose
"Sing a Song of Sixpence," Mother Goose
Six Dinner Sid by Inga Moore
The Five Senses by Aliki

Songs you can sing emphasizing initial /s/ are "Oh Susannah" and "You Are My Sunshine."

Thank you for your support. Please sign and return this when you have completed the above lessons.

Additional Teacher Comment *(optional):*

Parent signature _____

Please write your comments, if any, on the other side of this memo.

SID SEAL ACTIVITY PAGE

Circle the pictures that begin with /s/.

SID SEAL PUPPET PATTERNS

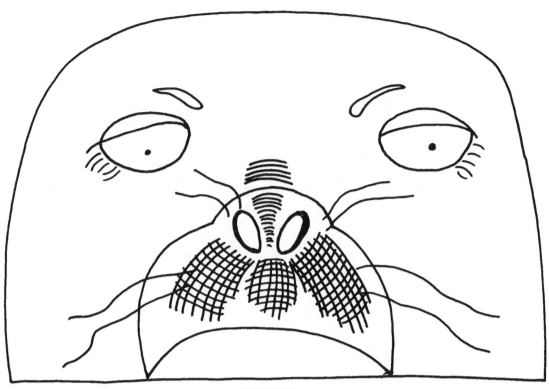

GRAY HEAD

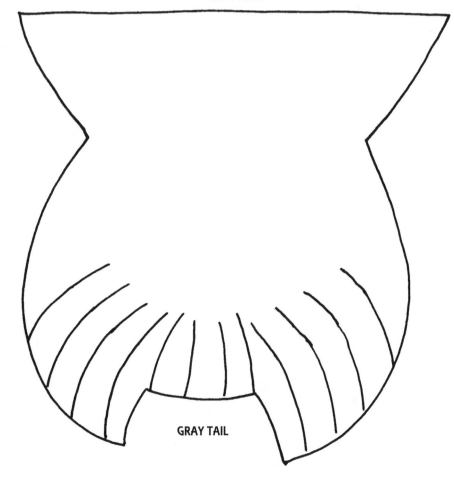

GRAY TAIL

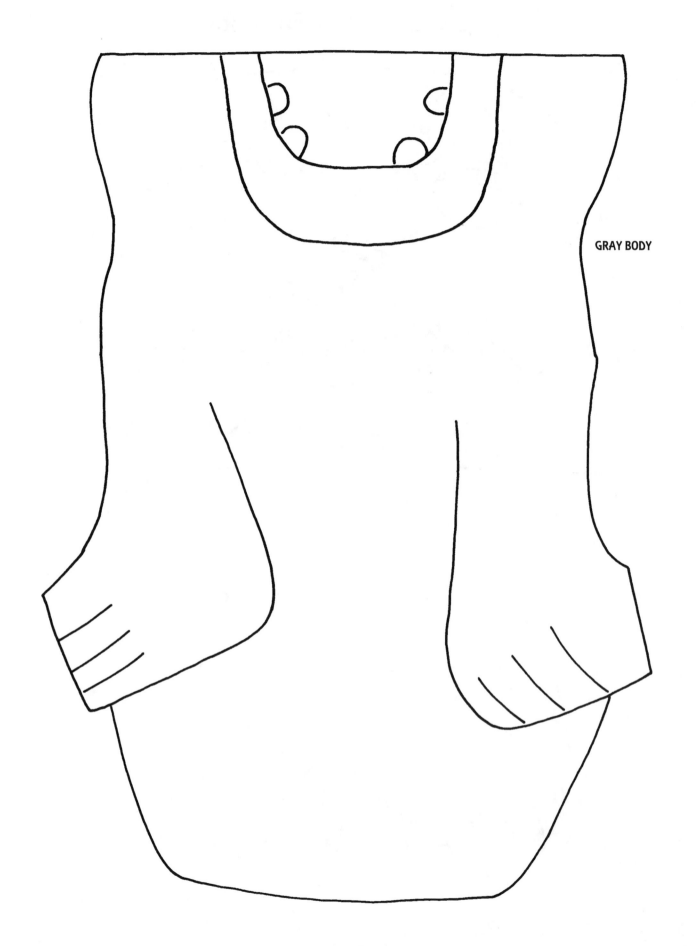

GRAY BODY

SID SEAL B&W FLANNEL BOARD FIGURE

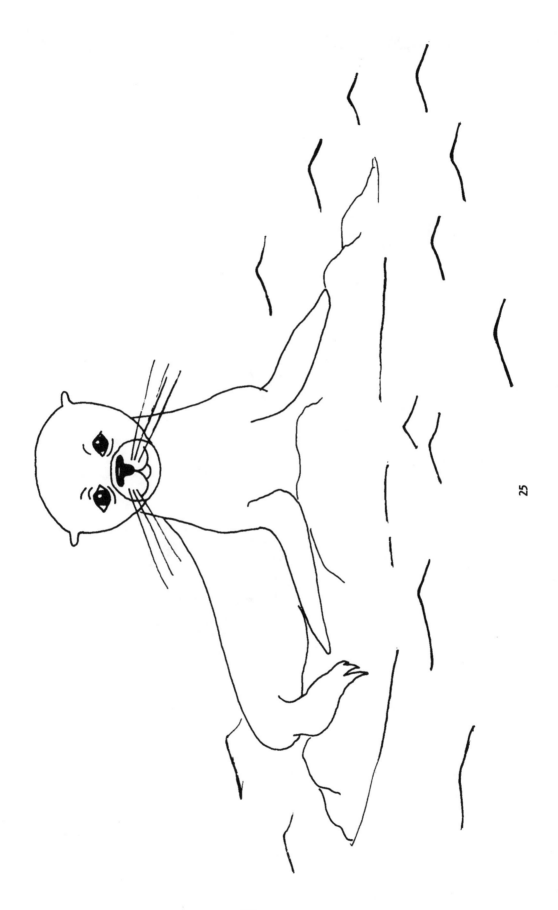

25

SID SEAL B&W FLANNEL BOARD FIGURE

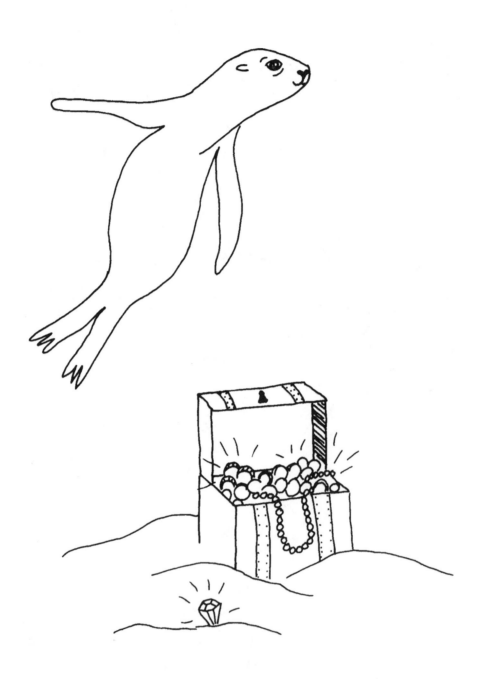

26

TIM TIGER

FLANNEL BOARD STORY

Tonight in Ring Two of the Big Top, see Tim Tiger tiptoe on the tightrope! *(figure 27)* Tell the town to gather in the turquoise tent to see Tim show his talent. He'll stand tall, show his teeth, and take off. It will be the talk of the town. Remember, to see Tim the Terrific Tiger, you need to be in the Big Top Tuesday at ten!

TIM TIGER SONG

(Can be sung to "The Bear Went Over the Mountain")

Tim Tiger tiptoes on the tightrope.
Tim Tiger tiptoes on the tightrope.
Tim Tiger tiptoes on the tightrope.
Tuesday night at ten, Tuesday night at ten.
Tim Tim Tiger tiptoes on the tightrope
Tuesday night at ten.

VOCABULARY

Initial /t/

ONE-SYLLABLE WORDS

talk	tan	tell	toe	town
tag	tank	ten	tongue	toy
tail	tap	tent	took	tune
take	tar	tide	top	turn
talk	taste	tight	torch	two
tall	teach	time	touch	type
tame	teeth	toast		

TWO-SYLLABLE WORDS

table	tasteful	ticket	tired	tuna
taco	tattle	tiger	today	turkey
talent	teapot	tightrope	tonight	turquoise
tangle	tender	tinsel	towel	turtle
target	tennis	tiny	tulip	

TIM TIGER PUPPET

Materials:

light golden brown construction paper;

black marker;

brown and white crayon;

2 cotton balls *(optional);*

lunch bag;

scissors;

glue

Directions:

1. Duplicate the patterns on construction paper. Cut off one inch from the bottom of the bag.

2. Outline the tiger in black. Color in stripes, inside of mouth, pupils of eyes, and nostrils. Color eyes and nose brown. Color teeth, tips of ears, and highlight in pupils of eyes white.

3. Glue onto bag. If desired, spread out cotton balls until they are very wispy. Glue on the back of the top part of the face. Glue around bottom of face to create a wispy mane effect.

PARENT MEMO

Today's date: _____

Child's name: _____

Dear Parent:

Please set aside five minutes a day to work on these exercises for initial /t/.

Please read these words to your child every day. Your child is to listen, but not repeat them to you.

tail	tar	tide	tongue	taco
talk	taste	toast	turn	tattle
tame	teeth	toe	type	turquoise

Your child should practice saying these each day. Check off each time he or she says the words to you.

tank
0 0 0 0 0

ten
0 0 0 0 0

tent
0 0 0 0 0

torch
0 0 0 0 0

toy
0 0 0 0 0

two
0 0 0 0 0

Helping your child with speech homework will be an important advantage for your child's progress. If your child experiences difficulty or frustration, stop. Try to make your sessions brief and positive. If you want to further enrich your child's speech program and language development, you might consider checking out any of the following books from the library and reading them with your child. They contain initial /t/ in the titles.

Tar Beach by Faith Ringgeia
Today Is Monday by Eric Carle
The Teeny, Tiny Woman by Paul Galdone
Yertle the Turtle by Dr. Seuss

Songs you can sing emphasizing initial /t/ are "I'm a Little Teapot" and "Ten Little Indians."

Thank you for your support. Please sign and return this when you have completed the above lessons.

Additional Teacher Comment *(optional):*

Parent signature _____

Please write your comments, if any, on the other side of this memo.

TIM TIGER ACTIVITY PAGE

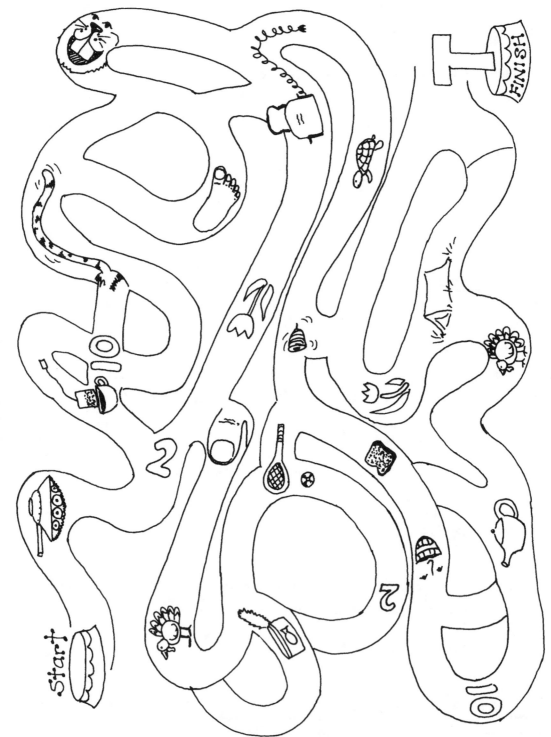

Find the way home by coloring the path with all /t/pictures.

©1996 by Elizabeth Krepelin and Bonnie Mae Smith

76

TIM TIGER PUPPET PATTERN

LIGHT BROWN

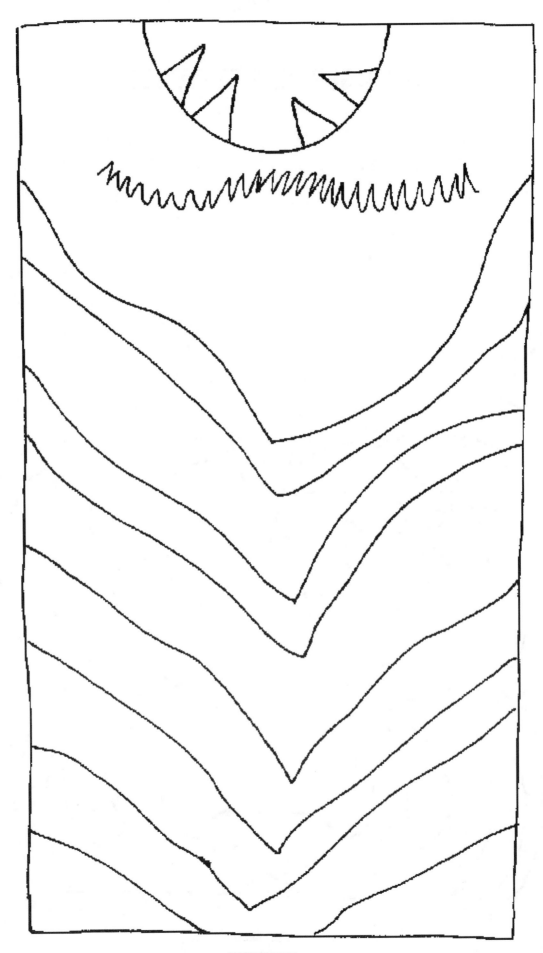

LIGHT BROWN

TIM TIGER B&W FLANNEL BOARD FIGURE

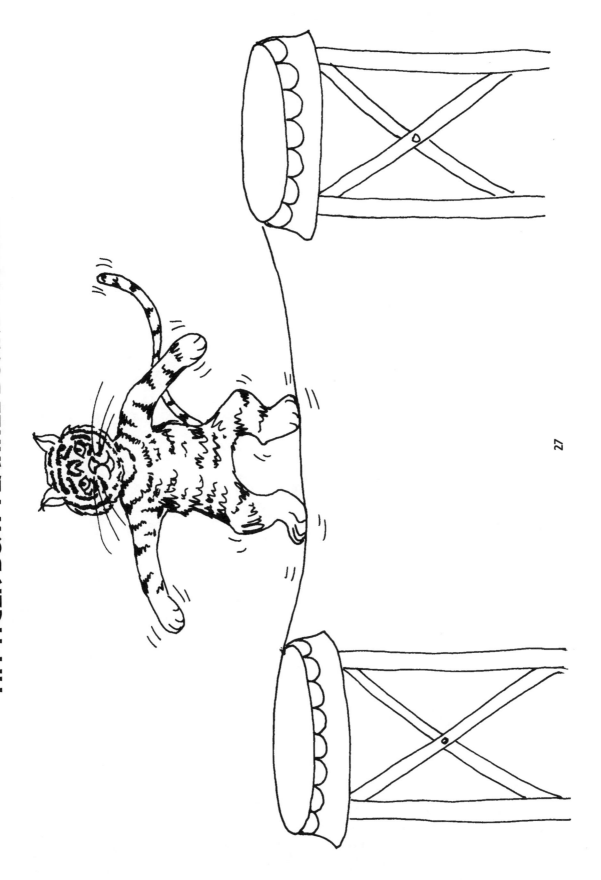

27

FINAL SINGLE
CONSONANT SOUNDS

BAB CRAB

FLANNEL BOARD STORY

Bab Crab just loves to gab! I wouldn't fib! She'd gab to a mob or a tiny spider in a web. *(figure 28)* She'd talk to a driver of a cab, a babe in a crib *(figure 29),* a crew on a sub, or a whole tribe. She's no snob! She'll hobnob with anyone on the globe. She should be careful not to blab to someone who grabs her for crab stew!

BAB CRAB SONG

(Can be sung to "Mary Had a Little Lamb")

Bab Crab loved to gab and blab,
Gab and blab, gab and blab.
Bab Crab loved to gab and blab
To creatures small and big.

She gabbed to a tiny babe
Tiny babe, tiny babe.
She gabbed to a tiny babe
And made the babe say goo.

She blabbed to a big tribe
Big tribe, big tribe.
She blabbed to a big tribe
Who made some Bab Crab stew.

VOCABULARY

Final /b/

ONE-SYLLABLE WORDS

babe	crab	gab	lab	scrub	throb
bib	crib	globe	mob	slob	tribe
blab	cub	glob	rib	snob	tub
bribe	ebb	grab	rob	sob	tube
cab	fib	grub	robe	stub	web
club	flab	jab	rub	sub	
cob	flub				

TWO-SYLLABLE WORDS

bathrobe	doorknob	hubbub	sparerib
bathtub	hobnob	prescribe	wardrobe
cobweb			

BAB CRAB PUPPET

Materials:

hot pink and pale pink construction paper;

oil pastels, crayons or markers;

lunch bag;

scissors;

glue

Directions:

1. Duplicate the patterns on construction paper. Cut off six inches from the bottom of the bag.

2. Outline all parts with a black crayon or marker. Use orange oil pastel to color in "whites" of eyes and black for the eyeball with a white dot for the pupil. Use orange oil pastel to color in claw on legs and pinchers. (Oil pastels have vibrant color, so they are the preferred medium for this whimsical puppet. Crayons or markers are fine, too.)

3. Cut out all parts. Glue bottom part of puppet on first, putting flat part even with top crease of inside of the bag. Line up mouth and glue on the top of the puppet. Glue legs to the side of the head (top part of the puppet).

PARENT MEMO

Today's date: _____

Child's name: _____

Dear Parent:

Please set aside five minutes a day to work on these exercises for final /b/.

Please read these words to your child every day. Your child is to listen, but not repeat them to you.

blab	crib	flub	rib	sob
bribe	doorknob	globe	scrub	stub
club	ebb	hubbub	slob	tube

Your child should practice saying these each day. Check off each time he or she says the words to you.

bib
0 0 0 0 0

club
0 0 0 0 0

crab
0 0 0 0 0

robe
0 0 0 0 0

tub
0 0 0 0 0

web
0 0 0 0 0

Helping your child with speech homework will be an important advantage for your child's progress. If your child experiences difficulty or frustration, stop. Try to make your sessions brief and positive. If you want to further enrich your child's speech program and language development, you might consider checking out any of the following books from the library and reading them with your child. They contain final /b/ in the titles.

Charlotte's Web by E. B. White
"Rub-a-Dub-Dub, Three Men in a Tub," Mother Goose

Thank you for your support. Please sign and return this when you have completed the above lessons.

Additional Teacher Comment *(optional):*

Parent signature _____

Please write your comments, if any, on the other side of this memo.

BAB CRAB ACTIVITY PAGE

Color the pictures that end in /b/.

BAB CRAB PUPPET PATTERN

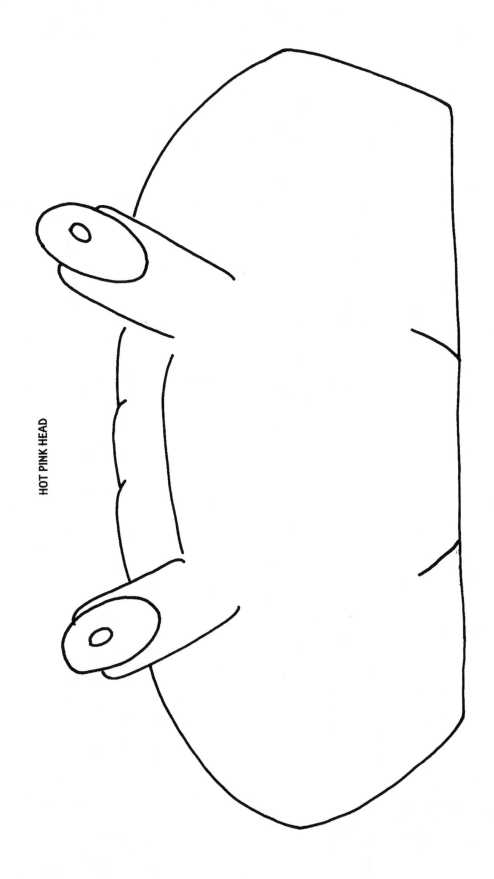

HOT PINK HEAD

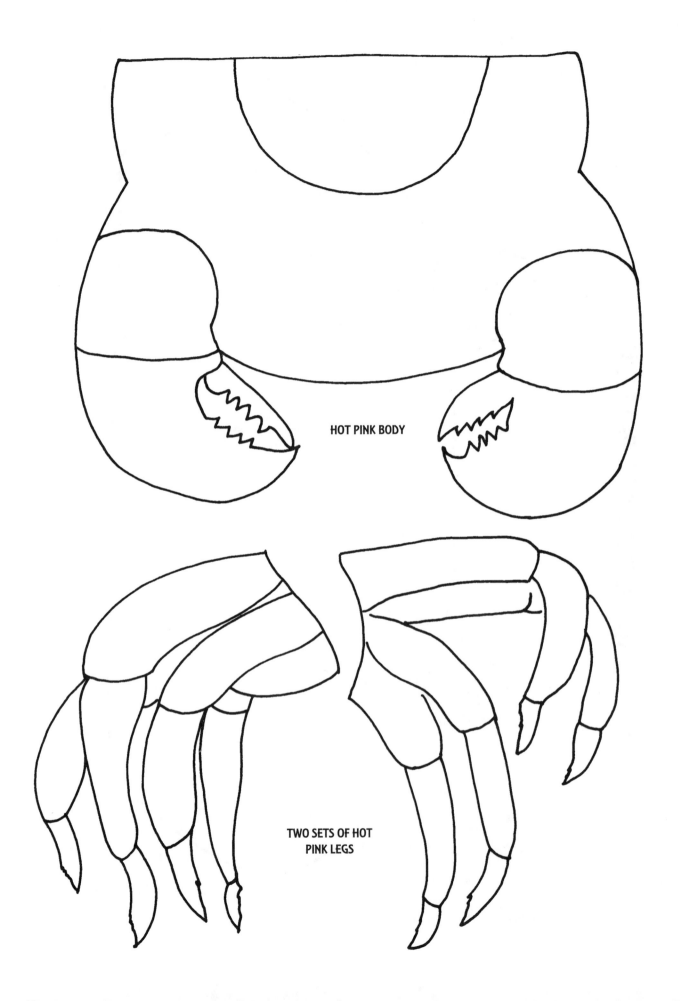

HOT PINK BODY

TWO SETS OF HOT
PINK LEGS

BAB CRAB B&W FLANNEL BOARD FIGURES

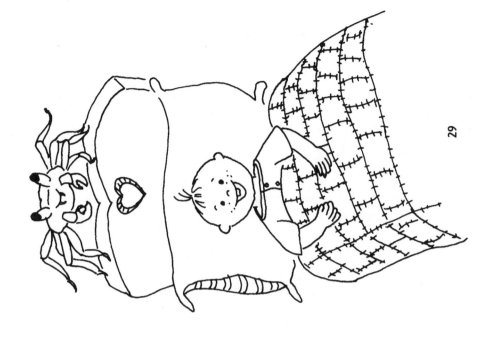

29

28

SPECK NECK

FLANNEL BOARD STORY

You've heard people speak about Disco Duck? Did you ever hear talk about Speck Neck, the giraffe who loved to rock? *(figure 30)* Check it out! Music was like magic to Speck. No joke! When he heard the beat he would shake his neck, his back, even his stomach. He was your basic rock machine. When Speck would rock, it would stop traffic for a block. *(figure 31)* Cars and trucks would put on their brakes and look. Horns would honk, squawk, and squeak. Everyone had to sneak a peek at Speck Neck, the rock-and-roll freak.

SPECK NECK SONG

(Can be sung to "Shake, Rattle and Roll")

Get out of that jungle and shake your back and neck.
Get out of that jungle and shake your back and neck.
Get out of that jungle and shake your back and neck.

I said shake, Speck, shake. I said shake, Speck, shake.
I said shake, Speck, shake. I said shake, Speck, shake.
You can shake and rock 'til your neck can nearly break.

VOCABULARY

Final /k/

ONE-SYLLABLE WORDS

ache	cheek	joke	pick	snake	
back	cluck	kick	quack	sneak	thick
bike	clock	knock	quake	sock	took
black	cook	lake	quick	speak	trick
block	duck	lick	rake	spook	truck
book	fake	like	sack	squeak	wake
break	flake	lock	sake	steak	walk
brick	freak	look	shake	stick	week
cake	hawk	neck	shock	strike	yolk
chalk	hike	pack	sick	take	
check	hook	peek	snack	talk	

TWO-SYLLABLE WORDS

alike	critic	frolic	lipstick	plastic
attack	cupcake	garlic	magic	rustic
basic	earache	headache	music	shamrock
broomstick	earthquake	hectic	outlook	stomach
chopstick	fabric	homesick	panic	traffic
clinic	frantic	lilac	peacock	yardstick

SPECK NECK PUPPET

Materials:

yellow construction paper;

brown, orange, and white crayons;

black marker;

lunch bag;

scissors;

glue

Directions:

1. Duplicate the patterns on construction paper. Cut off one inch from the bottom of the bag.

2. Outline entire figure with black marker. Fill in mouth on head and U-shaped lip with black marker. Fill in whites of eye with white crayon. Fill in spots, mane, and eyes with brown.

3. Cut out all parts. Glue on head, lining up bottom edge with flap edge. Glue on body, taking top edge all the way up to the crease in the bag. Line up mouth so top triangle makes mouth with U.

PARENT MEMO

Today's date: _____

Child's name: _____

Dear Parent:

Please set aside five minutes a day to work on these exercises for final /k/.

Please read these words to your child every day. Your child is to listen, but not repeat them to you.

bike	joke	magic	quick	spook
black	knock	peek	shamrock	squeak
hawk	like	quack	snake	truck

Your child should practice saying these each day. Check off each time he or she says the words to you.

block
O O O O O

book
O O O O O

cake
O O O O O

duck
O O O O O

clock
O O O O O

sack
O O O O O

Helping your child with speech homework will be an important advantage for your child's progress. If your child experiences difficulty or frustration, stop. Try to make your sessions brief and positive. If you want to further enrich your child's speech program and language development, you might consider checking out any of the following books from the library and reading them with your child. They contain final /k/ in the titles.

"Hickory, Dickory Dock," Mother Goose
Rosie's Walk by Pat Hutchins
Sand Cake by Frank Asch
The Cake That Mack Ate by Rose Robart
The Little Duck by Judy Dunn
The Magic School Bus by Joanna Cole

Songs you can sing emphasizing final /k/ are "Rock Around the Clock" and "Shake My Sillies Out."

Thank you for your support. Please sign and return this when you have completed the above lessons.

Additional Teacher Comment *(optional):*

Parent signature _____

Please write your comments, if any, on the other side of this memo.

SPECK NECK ACTIVITY PAGE

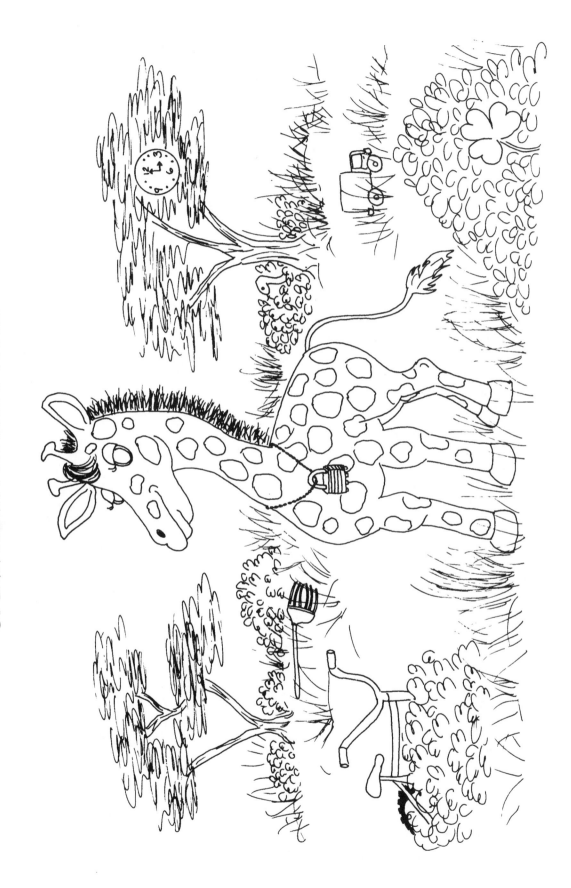

SPECK NECK PUPPET PATTERN

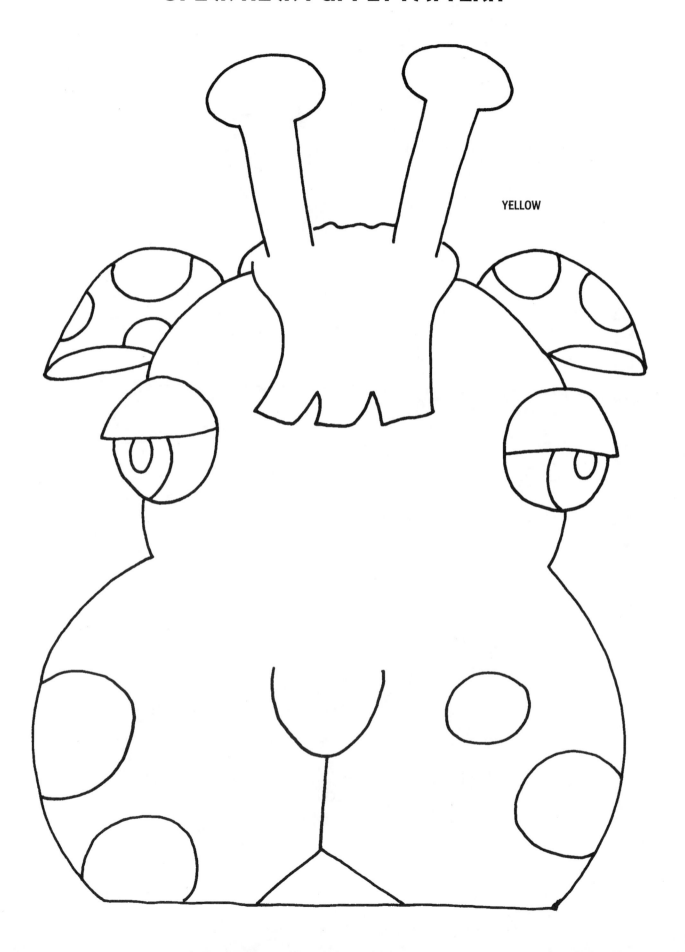

YELLOW

SPECK NECK PUPPET PATTERN

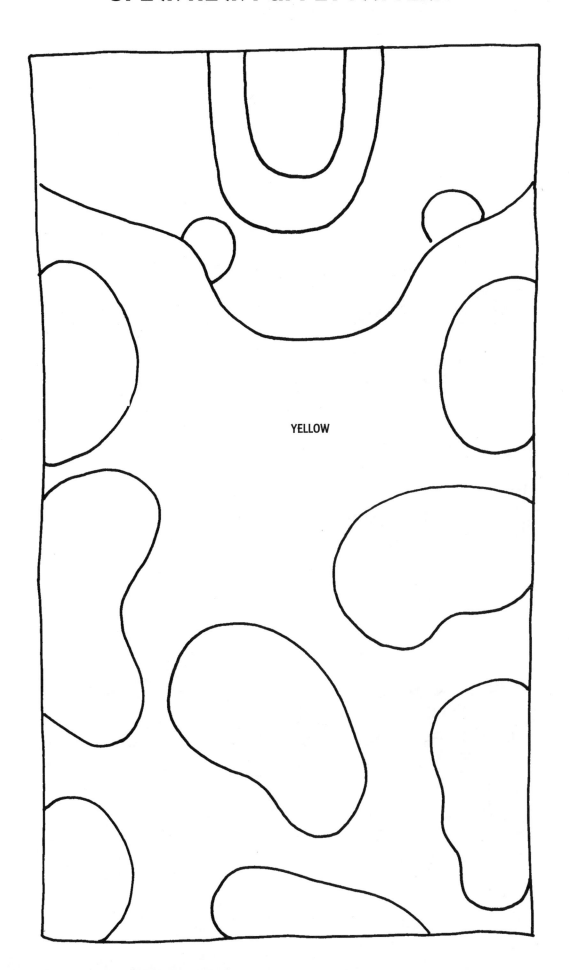

YELLOW

31

30

SAD TED

FLANNEL BOARD STORY

Poor Ted! He was a sad teddy bear. *(figure 32)* He cried and cried. He was given to a kid by his dad. The kid was afraid Ted would be ruined if they played outside. Instead, he put Ted on his bed. *(figure 33)* Ted felt like a dud. He was bored and filled with dread.

Then the kid got sick and had to head for bed. The kid read to Ted and fed him good food. *(figure 34)* He would pretend that Ted needed a band-aid. The kid became Ted's best bud. When he got well he didn't leave Ted behind. He took him outside. Ted was glad.

SAD TED SONG

(Can be sung to "In a Cabin in the Wood")

On a bed Sad Ted cried.
Teddy tears he could not hide.
Had a kid who played outside.
Leaving Ted alone.

"Boo hoo! Boo hoo!" Sad Ted cried.
"I need to be someone's pride."
"Come," the kid said, "by my side."
"Good buds, we'll abide."

VOCABULARY

Final /d/

ONE-SYLLABLE WORDS

add	cried	food	kid	paid	send
aid	dad	fried	lad	plaid	side
bad	dead	glad	load	pride	thud
bed	did	glide	loud	read	tide
bid	dread	good	mad	red	toad
blood	dud	grade	made	ride	wed
braid	dude	guide	mood	sad	weed
bread	fad	had	mud	sand	wood
bride	fade	head	need	seed	
cloud	feed	hide	nod	shade	
could	flood	hood	odd	should	

TWO-SYLLABLE WORDS

afraid	birdseed	divide	instead	salad
ahead	bobsled	elude	invade	seaweed
applaud	carload	hated	mermaid	stampede
avoid	charade	hayride	outside	succeed
beside	crusade	hillside	parade	

SAD TED PUPPET

Materials:

brown construction paper;

red or blue construction paper for bow;

brown and black crayons or markers;

lunch bag;

scissors;

glue

Directions:

1. Duplicate the patterns on construction paper. Cut off one inch from the bottom of the bag.

2. Color and outline eyes, nose, and mouth black. Outline stitches with brown. Outline and color in the top loops of the bow with a darker shade.

3. Cut out all pieces. Glue on head, lining up the bottom edge on the bottom of the bag flap. Glue on the body, lining up mouth. Glue on the bow. Glue on arms and legs, partly covering side edges of ribbon. The arms are short; the legs are long.

PARENT MEMO

Today's date: _____

Child's name: _____

Dear Parent:

Please set aside five minutes a day to work on these exercises for final /d/.

Please read these words to your child every day. Your child is to listen, but not repeat them to you.

braid	cloud	nod	sand	thud
bread	glide	odd	shade	tide
bride	mermaid	pride	stampede	weed

Your child should practice saying these each day. Check off each time he or she says the words to you.

bed
0 0 0 0 0

bride
0 0 0 0 0

cloud
0 0 0 0 0

seed
0 0 0 0 0

slide
0 0 0 0 0

toad
0 0 0 0 0

Helping your child with speech homework will be an important advantage for your child's progress. If your child experiences difficulty or frustration, stop. Try to make your sessions brief and positive. If you want to further enrich your child's speech program and language development, you might consider checking out any of the following books from the library and reading them with your child. They contain final /d/ in the titles.

Frog and Toad Are Friends by Arnold Lobel
Goodnight Moon by Margaret Wise Brown
Inside, Outside, Upside Down by Stan Berenstain and Janice Berenstain
Little Red Riding Hood by James Marshall
Sand Cake by Frank Asch
The Carrot Seed by Ruth Krauss

Songs you can sing emphasizing final /d/ are "In a Cabin in the Wood" and "Ten in a Bed."

Thank you for your support. Please sign and return this when you have completed the above lessons.

Additional Teacher Comment *(optional)*:

Parent signature _____

Please write your comments, if any, on the other side of this memo.

SAD TED ACTIVITY PAGE

Circle the pictures that end in /d/.

SAD TED PUPPET PATTERNS

SAD TED PUPPET PATTERN

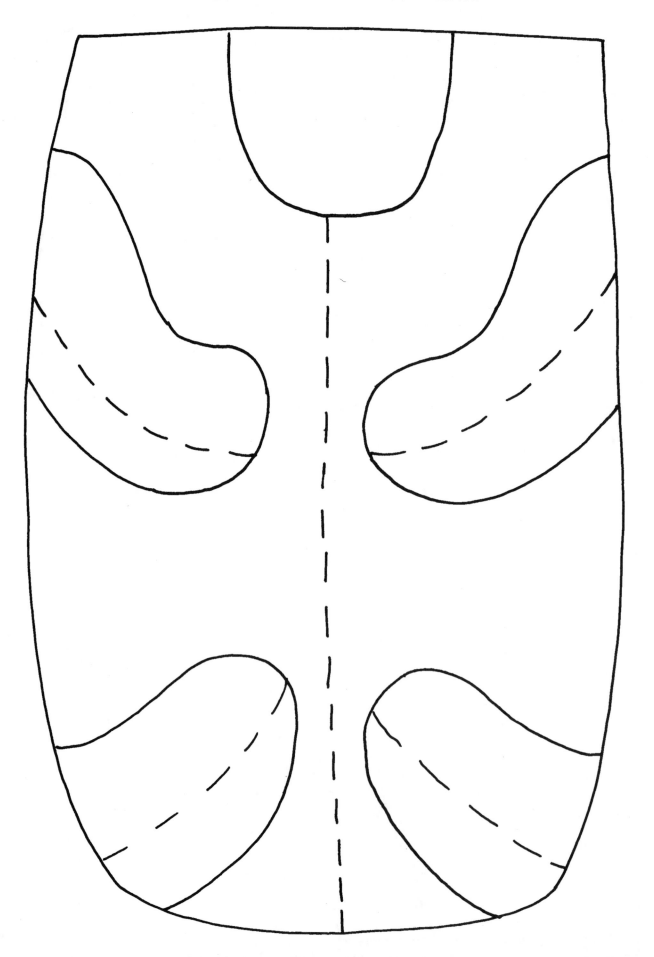

SAD TED B&W FLANNEL BOARD FIGURES

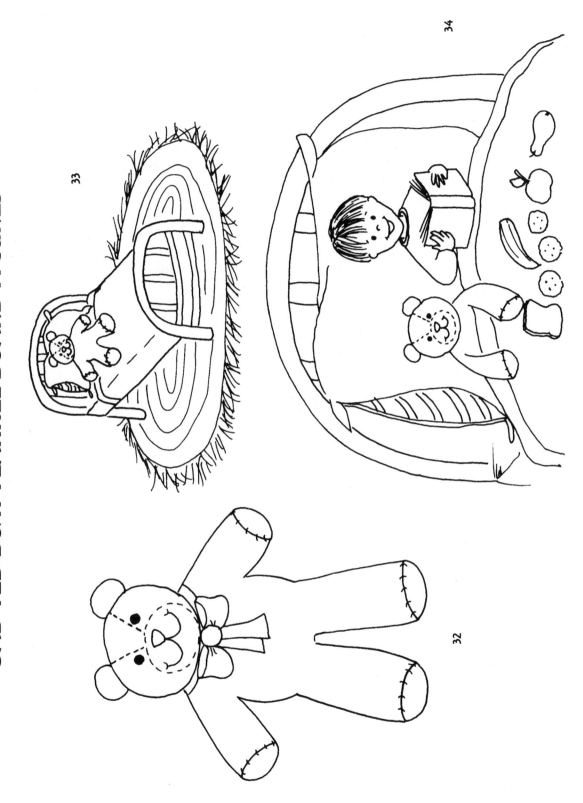

TIG PIG

FLANNEL BOARD STORY

Tig is from the famous Three Little Pig family. *(figure 35)* He is a smug pig, but he doesn't brag. Did he use straw to build his house? I beg your pardon! Did he use the twig plan? Dig this. He was the brick pig! When the big, bad wolf started to bug him, he didn't slug it out—he used what was under his wig. *(figure 36)* He put a log on the fire and the rest is history. Tig was one smart hog.

TIG PIG SONG

Can be sung to "My Darlin' Clementine")

Tig Pig, Tig Pig,
Made a fire with a log.
Big Bad Wolf Stew was for supper.
What a clever little hog!

VOCABULARY

Final /g/

ONE-SYLLABLE WORDS

bag	drag	hug	plug	smug
beg	dug	jug	rag	tag
big	egg	leg	rug	tug
bog	fig	log	sag	twig
brag	flag	mug	shrug	vague
bug	fog	peg	slug	wag
dig	frog	pig	smog	wig
dog	hog			

TWO-SYLLABLE WORDS

agog	bulldog	fatigue	ragtag	washrag
bedbug	eggnog	humbug	shindig	zigzag

TIG PIG PUPPET

Materials:

pink construction paper;

light bright colored construction paper;

black, red, white, and other bright colored crayons;

lunch bag;

scissors;

glue

Directions:

1. Duplicate the patterns on construction paper. Cut off three inches from the bottom of the bag.

2. Trace all parts with black. Color inside of ears with red; color cheeks red. Color inside of mouth black. Decorate brightly colored coveralls with various colored crayons as desired. Coveralls can also be traced onto wall paper, if preferred.

3. Cut out all pieces. Glue on head. The end flat edges line up on the edge of the top of the bag. The snout hangs down a bit, so be careful not to glue the mouth shut! Glue on body, lining up mouth. The top edge goes to the crease of the bag. Glue on coveralls. Glue arms to front of bag. Glue legs to the back of the coveralls, dimples facing forward.

PARENT MEMO

Today's date: _____

Child's name: _____

Dear Parent:

Please set aside five minutes a day to work on these exercises for final /g/.

Please read these words to your child every day. Your child is to listen, but not repeat them to you.

beg	egg	hug	sag	vague
brag	flag	mug	shrug	wag
dig	fog	plug	twig	zigzag

Your child should practice saying these each day. Check off each time he or she says the words to you.

bug
O O O O O

dog
O O O O O

egg
O O O O O

flag
O O O O O

frog
O O O O O

jug
O O O O O

Helping your child with speech homework will be an important advantage for your child's progress. If your child experiences difficulty or frustration, stop. Try to make your sessions brief and positive. If you want to further enrich your child's speech program and language development, you might consider checking out any of the following books from the library and reading them with your child. They contain final /g/ in the titles.

A Hole Is to Dig by Ruth Krauss
Frog and Toad Together by Arnold Lobel
The Enormous Egg by Roald Dahl
The Grouchy Ladybug by Eric Carle
Pig Pig Goes to Camp by David McPhail

Songs you can sing emphasizing final /g/ are "You're a Grand Old Flag" and "Frog Went a Courtin'."

Thank you for your support. Please sign and return this when you have completed the above lessons.

Additional Teacher Comment *(optional):*

Parent signature _____

Please write your comments, if any, on the other side of this memo.

TIG PIG ACTIVITY PAGE

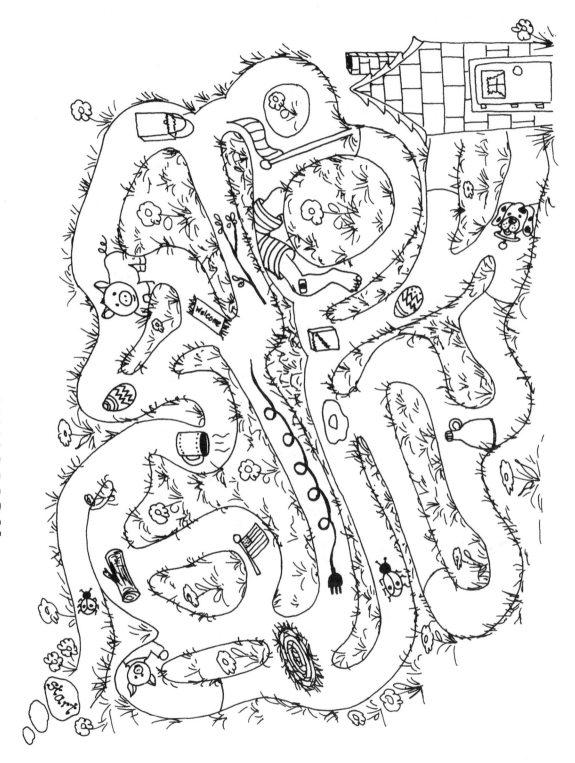

Color the pictures that end in /g/ to find the path to Tig's house.

TIG PIG PUPPET PATTERNS

PINK

PINK LEGS

TIG PIG PUPPET PATTERNS

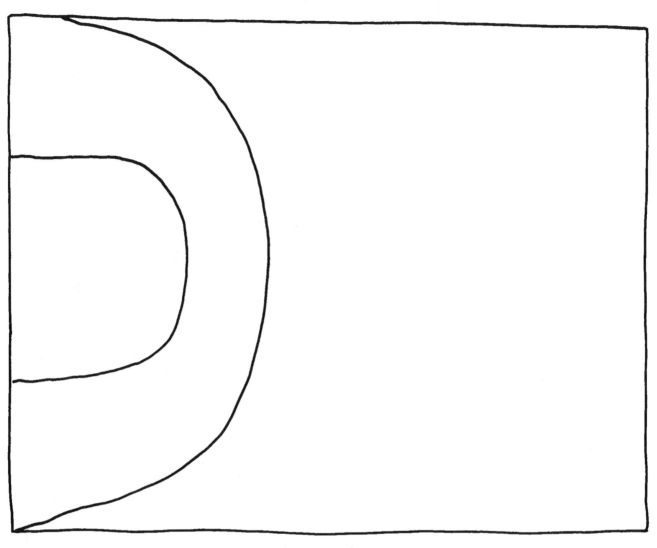

(TOP OF BODY) PINK

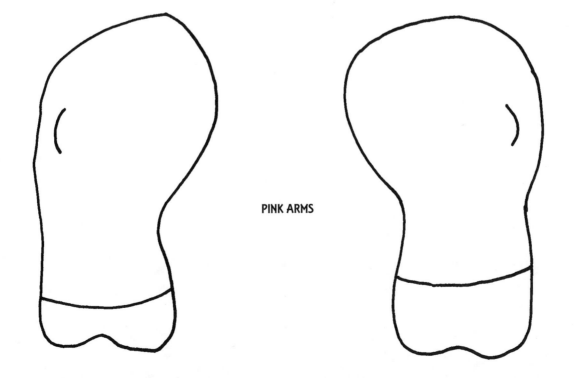

PINK ARMS

TIG PIG PUPPET PATTERN

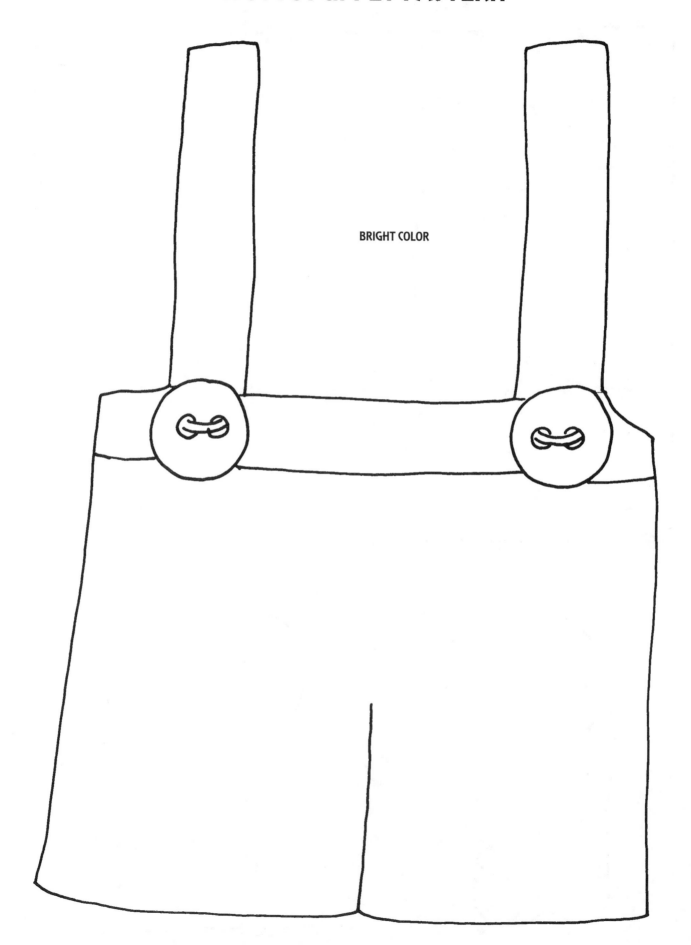

BRIGHT COLOR

TIG PIG B&W FLANNEL BOARD FIGURES

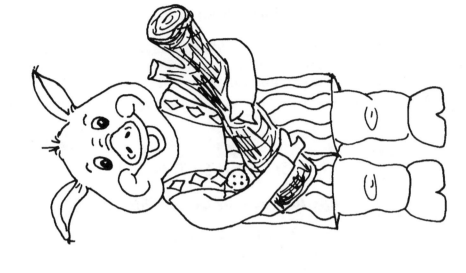

36

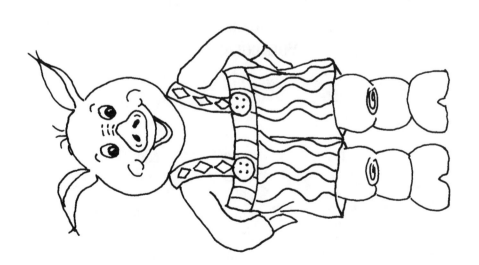

35

111

SAL CAMEL

FLANNEL BOARD STORY

Sal is a faithful camel with muscle. *(figure 37)* He has to toil in the hot soil, but he is joyful. He will haul a jewel, a barrel of oil or mail on the trail, mile after mile. He will smile and yell, "Pile it on! I'm tall and full of style. I'll never fail. Life is never dull. I'll travel up hill and down dale." Sal is so special, he is now the royal camel of the queen. *(figure 38)*

SAL CAMEL SONG

(Can be sung to "Caissons Go Marching Along")

Over hill, over dale,
He will travel dusty trails.
Sal Camel is movin' along.

He's so strong and so cool,
He was tops in camel school.
Sal Camel is movin' along.

Oh it's loyal, royal he
In the desert sand you'll see,
Sal is well above the rest.
And where ere he goes
You will always know
Sal Camel is movin' along.

VOCABULARY

Final /l/

Oɴᴇ-sʏʟʟᴀʙʟᴇ ᴡᴏʀᴅs

all	fill	<u>mile</u>	school	<u>squeal</u>
ball	foil	oil	<u>scowl</u>	stale
<u>boil</u>	fool	owl	sell	still
bowl	full	pail	small	style
call	hall	<u>pool</u>	<u>smell</u>	tail
<u>cool</u>	hill	pull	<u>smile</u>	tall
<u>crawl</u>	<u>jail</u>	rail	snail	<u>thrill</u>
doll	kneel	real	spell	trail
fall	mail	role	spoil	whale
<u>feel</u>	meal	sail	<u>spool</u>	

Two-syllable words

airmail	corral	female	<u>muscle</u>	tadpole
April	cruel	football	oatmeal	tinfoil
baseball	detail	fragile	pastel	toenail
cancel	dial	hotel	pencil	towel
cartwheel	eggshell	jewell	refill	until
conceal	exhale	joyful	reptile	vowel
control	faithful	motel	royal	<u>windmill</u>

SAL CAMEL PUPPET

Materials:

brown construction paper;

black crayon or marker;

yellow crayon;

white crayon (or oil pastel);

lunch bag;

scissors;

glue

Directions:

1. Duplicate the patterns on construction paper. Cut off one inch from the bottom of the bag.

2. Outline with black. Fill in nostrils, eyeball, and triangle mouth with black. Color eye yellow and make a little white highlight in each eye.

3. Cut out the pieces. Glue head to top of bag, lining up flat edge with the flap. Glue on body, lining up head.

PARENT MEMO

Today's date: _____

Child's name: _____

Dear Parent:

Please set aside five minutes a day to work on these exercises for final /l/.

Please read these words to your child every day. Your child is to listen, but not repeat them to you.

boil	feel	muscle	smell	squeal
cool	jail	pool	smile	thrill
crawl	mile	scowl	spool	windmill

Your child should practice saying these each day. Check off each time he or she says the words to you.

ball
O O O O O

bell
O O O O O

doll
O O O O O

owl
O O O O O

shell
O O O O O

snail
O O O O O

Helping your child with speech homework will be an important advantage for your child's progress. If your child experiences difficulty or frustration, stop. Try to make your sessions brief and positive. If you want to further enrich your child's speech program and language development, you might consider checking out any of the following books from the library and reading them with your child. They contain final /l/ in the titles.

"Jack and Jill," Mother Goose
"Old King Cole," Mother Goose
Mc Gilligot's Pool by Dr. Seuss
The Snail's Spell by Joanne Ryder
William's Doll by Charlotte Zolotow

Songs you can sing emphasizing final /l/ are "School Days," "Take Me Out to the Ball Game" and "Rosie the Camel."

Thank you for your support. Please sign and return this when you have completed the above lessons.

Additional Teacher Comment *(optional):*

Parent signature _____

Please write your comments, if any, on the other side of this memo.

SAL CAMEL ACTIVITY PAGE

Color the pictures that end in /l/.

115

SAL CAMEL PUPPET PATTERN

BROWN

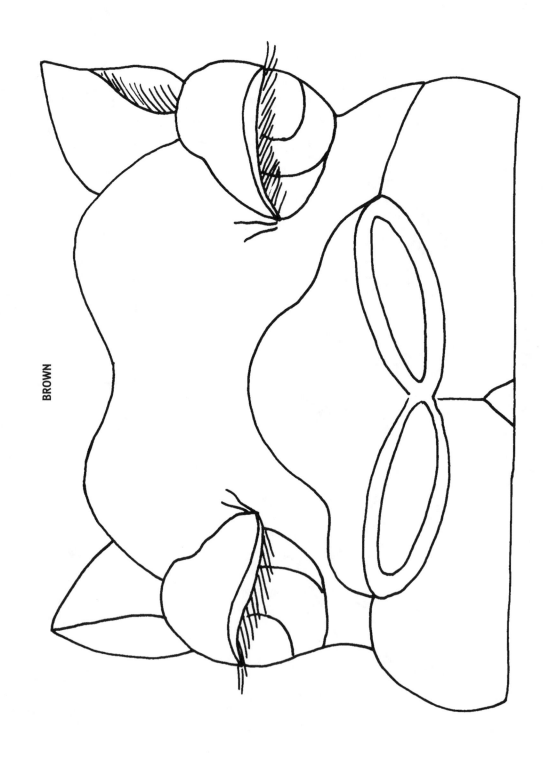

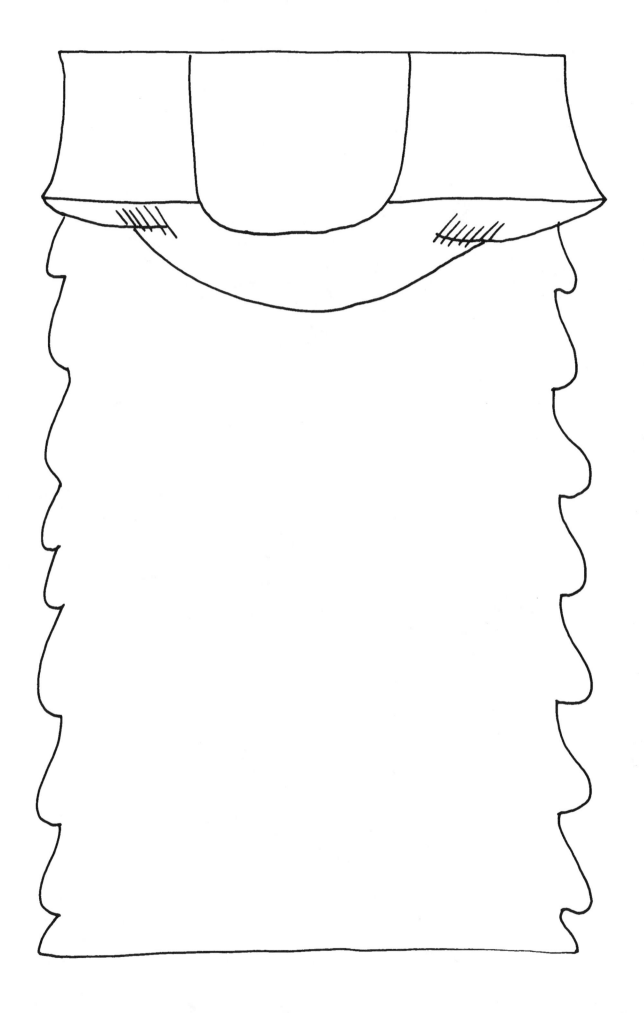

SAL CAMEL B&W FLANNEL BOARD FIGURES

37

38

SAM LAMB

FLANNEL BOARD STORY

Did you know Mary's lamb had a name? *(figure 39)* It was Sam. Sam was no bum! It may seem he broke the rules, but he was not to blame! He was so tame. His aim was to spend more time with Mary. So when she left home for school one day, Sam came too. *(figure 40)* School was never the same. That's how Sam gained fame. You know the rhyme!

SAM LAMB SONG

(Can be sung to "Skip to My Lou")

Sam Lamb, stay home,
Sam Lamb, stay home,
Sam Lamb, stay home.
Stay home, Sam Lamb!

Sam Lamb, don't roam,
Sam Lamb, don't roam,
Sam Lamb, don't roam,
Don't roam, Sam Lamb!

VOCABULARY

Final /m/

ONE-SYLLABLE WORDS

aim	came	gleam	lime	seem	tame
am	dime	gloom	name	shame	team
beam	doom	grim	palm	slam	them
blame	dream	gum	plum	slime	thumb
bloom	fame	ham	prim	some	time
boom	flame	hem	rhyme	stem	trim
broom	frame	home	room	sum	whim
bum	from	hum	scream	swim	zoom
calm	game	lamb			

TWO-SYLLABLE WORDS

album	bottom	income	phantom	supreme
bathroom	custom	lifetime	problem	symptom
became	denim	moonbeam	redeem	system
blossom	extreme	mushroom	sunbeam	wholesome

SAM LAMB PUPPET

Materials:

white construction paper;

black construction paper;

black, white, and brown crayons;

carbon paper;

cotton balls *(optional);*

lunch bag;

scissors;

glue

Directions:

1. Duplicate the patterns on construction paper. Cut off one inch from the bottom of the bag.

2. Using carbon paper, trace ears and two small parts of face on black construction paper. These lines are visible on the black construction paper. The white portions can be duplicated on a machine. Color the eyes brown, leaving the pupil black. Trace the nose and mouth with white crayon. Trace the curved lines on the white body with black.

3. Cut out all parts. Glue on top white head, lining up flat edge with edge of bag flap. Glue on white body. Cut dotted line of ears and fold. Glue at cut edge to make folded ears. Let ears dry. Put black face on lower center part of bag top. Line up black mouth inside of crease on the bottom of the bag and line it up with the top of the face. Glue on. Glue ears on top sides of face so they fit close to the head by the eyes. The fold of the ear should be on top. Spread out a cotton ball or two so they are fluffy and glue to the top of the head.

PARENT MEMO

Today's date: _____

Child's name: _____

Dear Parent:

Please set aside five minutes a day to work on these exercises for final /m/.

Please read these words to your child every day. Your child is to listen, but not repeat them to you.

bloom	calm	flame	ham	plum
blossom	dime	gleam	home	scream
broom	dream	gum	moonbeam	zoom

Your child should practice saying these each day. Check off each time he or she says the words to you.

broom
0 0 0 0 0

drum
0 0 0 0 0

frame
0 0 0 0 0

lime
0 0 0 0 0

palm
0 0 0 0 0

plum
0 0 0 0 0

Helping your child with speech homework will be an important advantage for your child's progress. If your child experiences difficulty or frustration, stop. Try to make your sessions brief and positive. If you want to further enrich your child's speech program and language development, you might consider checking out any of the following books from the library and reading them with your child. They contain final /m/ in the titles.

Green Eggs and Ham by Dr. Seuss
Moon Game by Frank Asch
Our Animal Friends at Maple Hill Farm by Alice and Martin Provensen

A song you can sing emphasizing final /m/ is "Mary Had a Little Lamb."

Thank you for your support. Please sign and return this when you have completed the above lessons.

Additional Teacher Comment *(optional):*

Parent signature _____

Please write your comments, if any, on the other side of this memo.

SAM LAMB ACTIVITY PAGE

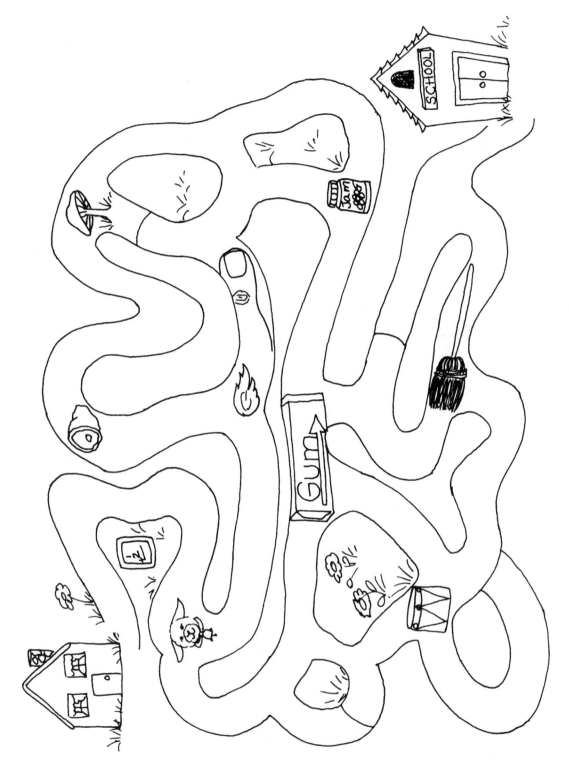

Color the pictures that end in /m/ to find the path to school.

SAM LAMB PUPPET PATTERNS

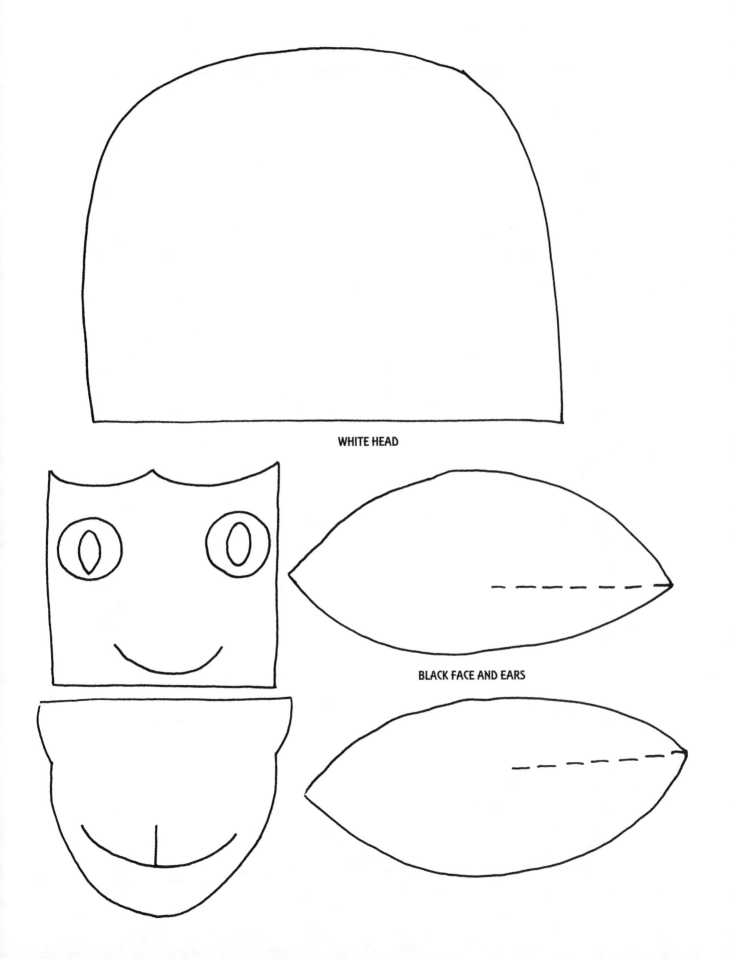

WHITE HEAD

BLACK FACE AND EARS

SAM LAMB PUPPET PATTERN

WHITE BODY

SAM LAMB B&W FLANNEL BOARD FIGURES

39

40

KEN LION

FLANNEL BOARD STORY

Ken Lion was a vegetarian. *(figure 41)* What I mean is, he would eat a pecan or a bean, an ice cream cone, a candy cane, a lawn—anything green grown under the sun. He would eat nothing with skin—not a swine, a swan, a hen, a robin, a raccoon, or a chicken. He certainly would not eat anything human like men, women, or children. All the African animals wore a grin and thought being a vegetarian lion was a fine plan for Ken!

KEN LION'S SONG

(Can be sung to "I'm a Little Teapot")

I'm a vegetarian, I like green—
Lawns and grapes and string beans.
When I see a salad bar I will run.
I'm first in line and eat a ton!

VOCABULARY

Final /n/

ONE-SYLLABLE WORDS

bean	done	hen	pan	soon	thin
bone	down	in	pen	spin	ton
brain	fan	lawn	phone	spine	town
brown	fin	line	pine	spoon	train
can	fine	loan	plane	stain	twin
chin	fun	main	rain	stone	van
clean	gain	man	run	sun	vine
clown	gone	mean	shine	swan	win
cone	green	moon	sign	swine	won
crown	grin	one	sin	tan	zone
dawn	grown	pain	skin	ten	

TWO-SYLLABLE WORDS

again	cabin	explain	napkin	rotten
airplane	chicken	fortune	ocean	ruin
alone	children	human	open	satin
bacon	clothespin	lion	pecan	seven
balloon	design	listen	prison	sunshine
begin	divine	lotion	raccoon	wagon
between	dragon	machine	ribbon	woman
button	engine	motion	robin	

KEN LION PUPPET

Materials:

light brown construction paper;

green, black, brown, and white crayons;

lunch bag;

scissors;

glue

Directions:

1. Duplicate the patterns on construction paper. Cut off one inch from the bottom of the bag.

2. Outline the lion with brown. Color black ring around eye. Color top of eye white and color the muzzle and chin (top and bottom of puppet) white. Color teeth white. Color nostrils dark brown. Color eyes green with black dot for pupil. Color inside of the mouth black. Using black and brown crayons, make vertical sweeping lines for mane.

3. Cut out all parts. Glue bottom of puppet to the bag all the way up to the crease. Line up flat edge of lion to bottom edge of bag and match up muzzle and glue on.

PARENT MEMO

Today's date: _____

Child's name: _____

Dear Parent:

Please set aside five minutes a day to work on these exercises for final /n/.

Please read these words to your child every day. Your child is to listen, but not repeat them to you.

brain	dragon	lawn	rain	train
brown	fun	phone	shine	twin
dawn	green	raccoon	spine	zone

Your child should practice saying these each day. Check off each time he or she says the words to you.

cane
0 0 0 0 0

clown
0 0 0 0 0

fan
0 0 0 0 0

moon
0 0 0 0 0

sun
0 0 0 0 0

ten
0 0 0 0 0

Helping your child with speech homework will be an important advantage for your child's progress. If your child experiences difficulty or frustration, stop. Try to make your sessions brief and positive. If you want to further enrich your child's speech program and language development, you might consider checking out any of the following books from the library and reading them with your child. They contain final /n/ in the titles.

Goodnight Moon by Margaret Wise Brown
Rain Makes Applesauce by Julian Scheer
Little Raccoon and the Thing in the Pool by Susan C. Poskanzer
The Little Engine That Could (any version)
The Little Red Hen (any version)
The Wolf's Chicken Stew by Keiko Kasza

Songs you can sing emphasizing final /n/ are "London Bridge Is Falling Down," "You Are My Sunshine," "This Old Man," and "In a Cabin in the Wood."

Thank you for your support. Please sign and return this when you have completed the above lessons.

Additional Teacher Comment *(optional)*:

Parent signature _____

Please write your comments, if any, on the other side of this memo.

KEN LION ACTIVITY PAGE

Color the pictures that end in /n/.

KEN LION PUPPET PATTERN

KEN LION PUPPET PATTERN

BROWN

KEN LION B&W FLANNEL BOARD FIGURE

41

BEBOP APE

FLANNEL BOARD STORY

Bebop Ape will keep going and not stop! Zap! He will bop and dip the latest dance step. *(figure 42)* Next time you check up on him he is doing the hula hoop *(figure 43),* but before you can clap he's on top of the high dive doing a deep leap or a daring jump. *(figure 44)* He can walk a tightrope or leap a loop on the trapeze and escape without a scrape. He can gallop, rope, and roundup at the rodeo without a mishap. Bebop has so much pep and he's in great shape. Will he poop out? Does he sleep or nap? Nope! Bebop will never droop. He has more pep than any ape on the map!

BEBOP APE SONG

(Can be sung to "London Bridge")

Bebop Ape can hula hoop,
Hula hoop, hula hoop.
Bebop Ape can hoola hoop,
Don't stop, Bebop!

Bebop Ape can jump and leap,
Jump and leap, jump and leap.
Bebop Ape can jump and leap,
Don't stop, Bebop!

Bebop Ape can gallop and rope,
Gallop and rope, gallop and rope.
Bebop Ape can gallop and rope,
Don't stop, Bebop!

VOCABULARY

Final /p/

ONE-SYLLABLE WORDS

ape	crop	heap	loop	rap	soap
<u>beep</u>	cup	hoop	map	ripe	<u>soup</u>
bop	<u>deep</u>	hope	<u>mop</u>	rope	steep
cap	dip	jeep	mope	scoop	step
<u>cape</u>	<u>droop</u>	jump	nap	scrape	<u>stop</u>
<u>cheap</u>	flip	keep	nip	shape	<u>stripe</u>
clap	flop	lap	peep	sheep	top
cop	gap	leap	pep	shop	up
<u>creep</u>	<u>group</u>	lip	pop	<u>sleep</u>	zap

TWO-SYLLABLE WORDS

bebop	footstep	mishap	tightrope	whitecap
checkup	gallop	roundup	tulip	windpipe
doorstep	gumdrop	syrup	turnip	workshop
escape	hilltop	teacup	unwrap	worship

BEBOP APE PUPPET

Materials:

brown construction paper;

bright colored construction paper;

crayons or marking pens;

lunch bag;

scissors;

glue

Directions:

1. Duplicate the patterns on construction paper. Cut off one inch from the bottom of the bag.

2. Outline all parts. Color in eyes and nostrils with black. Color tongue pink and nails peach.

3. Decorate shorts as desired.

4. Cut out all parts and glue onto bag. Glue on arms last.

PARENT MEMO

Today's date: _____

Child's name: _____

Dear Parent:

Please set aside five minutes a day to work on these exercises for final /p/.

Please read these words to your child every day. Your child is to listen, but not repeat them to you.

beep	creep	escape	mop	stop
cape	deep	gallop	sleep	stripe
cheap	droop	group	soup	tulip

Your child should practice saying these each day. Check off each time he or she says the words to you.

cap
0 0 0 0 0

cup
0 0 0 0 0

map
0 0 0 0 0

mop
0 0 0 0 0

rope
0 0 0 0 0

top
0 0 0 0 0

Helping your child with speech homework will be an important advantage for your child's progress. If your child experiences difficulty or frustration, stop. Try to make your sessions brief and positive. If you want to further enrich your child's speech program and language development, you might consider checking out any of the following books from the library and reading them with your child. They contain final /p/ in the titles.

Hop on Pop by Dr. Seuss
Sheep in a Jeep by Nancy Shaw
Stone Soup by Marcia Brown
Ten Apples Up on Top by Theodore LeSieg
The Enormous Turnip illustrated by Kathy Parkinson

Songs you can sing emphasizing final /p/ are "Skip to My Lou" and "On Top of Spaghetti."

Thank you for your support. Please sign and return this when you have completed the above lessons.

Additional Teacher Comment *(optional)*:

Parent signature _____

Please write your comments, if any, on the other side of this memo.

BEPOP APE ACTIVITY PAGE

Color the pictures that end in /p/.

©1996 by Elizabeth Krepelin and Bonnie Mae Smith

136

BEPOP APE PUPPET PATTERNS

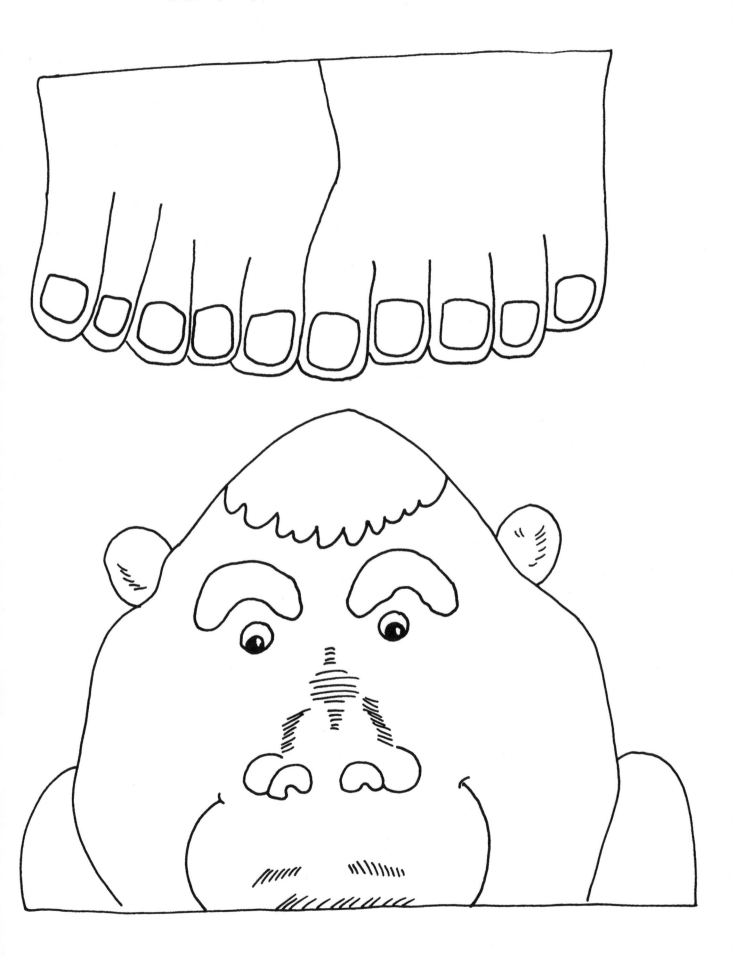

BEPOP APE PUPPET PATTERN

BEPOP APE PUPPET PATTERN

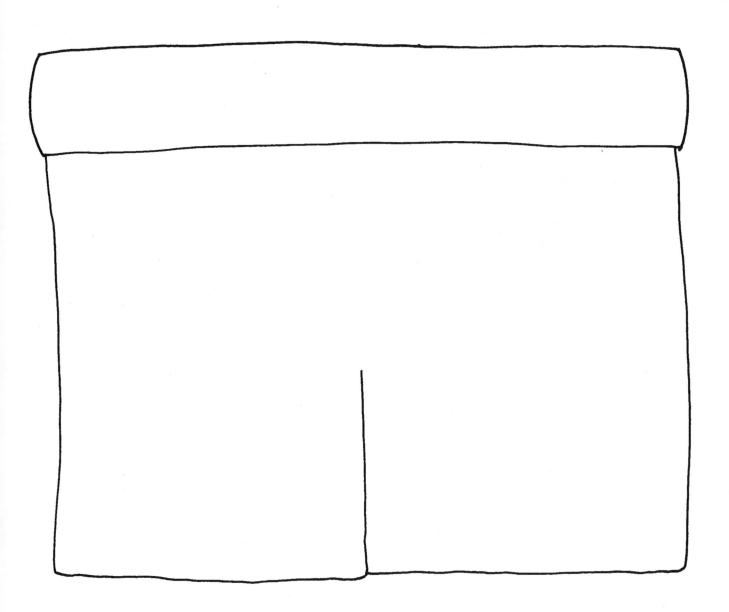

SHORTS—BRIGHT COLOR

BEPOP APE PUPPET PATTERN

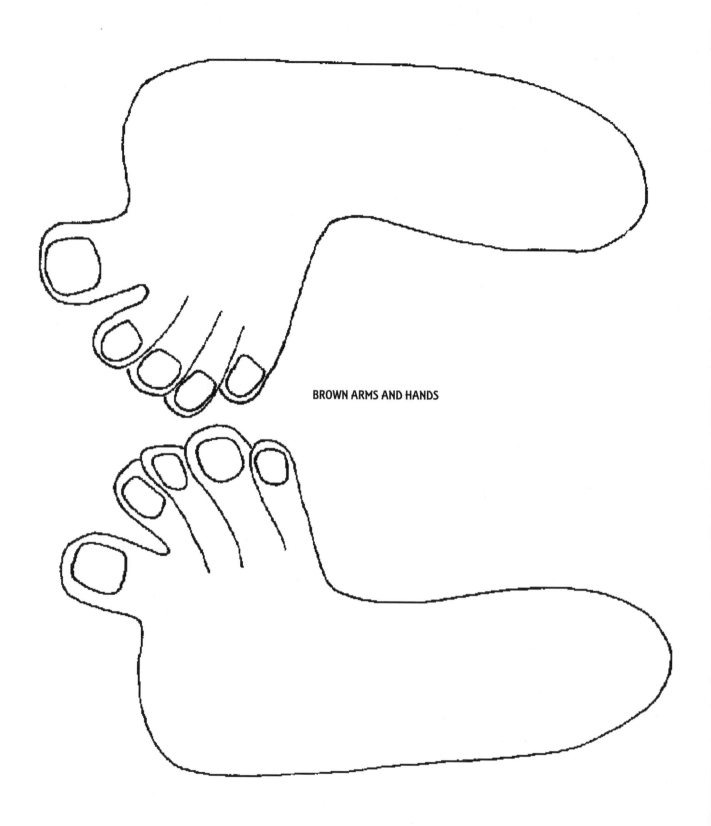

BROWN ARMS AND HANDS

BEPOP APE B&W FLANNEL BOARD FIGURES

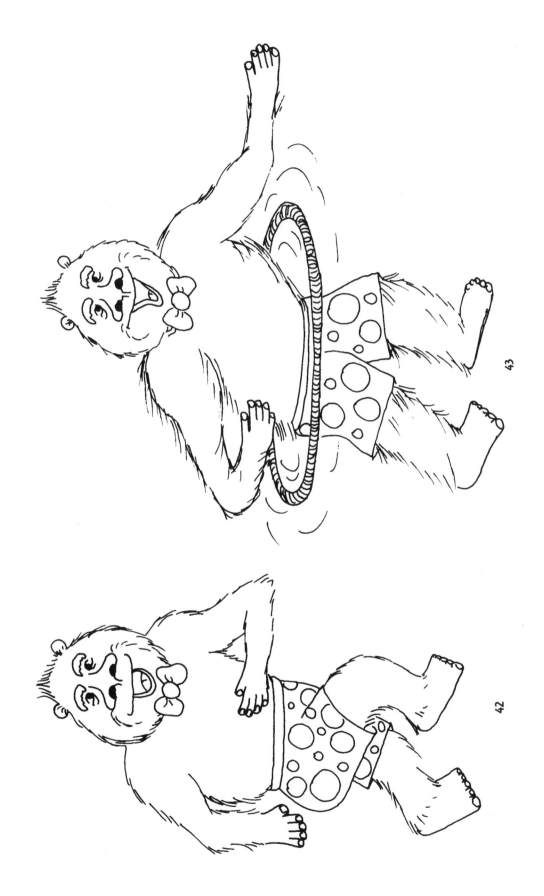

43

42

BEPOP APE B&W FLANNEL BOARD FIGURE

44

GRR VAMPIRE

FLANNEL BOARD STORY

Oh dear! Beware! I fear Grr Vampire might scare you. *(figure 45)* He sure does appear to be a vampire. He wears a black suit. He has sharp teeth. He wears a sour sneer. But wait! Hear more. Today is the thirty-first of October! Prepare yourself with a treat to share before you open the door. *(figure 46)* Grr Vampire might be there to scare you on this one night of the year.

GRR VAMPIRE SONG

(Can be sung to "'Dem Bones")

Grr Vampire, you're near
Grr Vampire, you're near
Grr Vampire, you're near
Beware! Beware! Beware!

VOCABULARY

Final /r/

ONE-SYLLABLE WORDS

air	ear	hear	<u>purr</u>	<u>stir</u>
bear	fair	her	<u>scare</u>	sure
car	far	<u>hour</u>	<u>share</u>	tire
<u>care</u>	fear	jar	smear	tour
<u>cheer</u>	fire	more	<u>sneer</u>	war
clear	<u>floor</u>	near	<u>sour</u>	wear
<u>dare</u>	four	or	spur	<u>whir</u>
dear	<u>fur</u>	pear	stair	year
door	hair	poor	star	your

TWO-SYLLABLE WORDS

admire	campfire	explore	indoor	umpire
adore	cashier	frontier	nowhere	unfair
ajar	compare	galore	outdoor	vampire
before	<u>detour</u>	<u>guitar</u>	seashore	
beware	downpour	ignore	secure	

GRR VAMPIRE PUPPET

Materials:

white construction paper;

crayons, preferably marking pens, in black,
     green, lavender, brown, and red;

lunch bag;

scissors;

glue

Directions:

1. Duplicate the patterns on construction paper. Cut off one inch from the bottom
   of the bag.

2. Outline eyes and nose with black. Color hat black. Color pants and coat black.
   Color the inside of the mouth and hatband red. Color shoes brown. Color tie
   purple. Skin should be green or lavender.

3. Cut out all parts. Glue on head. Glue on hat. Glue on bottom of figure, carefully lining up the mouth. Glue on bottom of legs and arms in "Boo" position.

PARENT MEMO

Today's date: _____

Child's name: _____

Dear Parent:

Please set aside five minutes a day to work on these exercises for final /r/.

Please read these words to your child every day. Your child is to listen, but not repeat them to you.

care	detour	guitar	scare	sour
cheer	floor	hour	share	stir
dare	fur	purr	sneer	whir

Your child should practice saying these each day. Check off each time he or she says the words to you.

bear
O O O O O

car
O O O O O

fire
O O O O O

four
O O O O O

pear
O O O O O

star
O O O O O

Helping your child with speech homework will be an important advantage for your child's progress. If your child experiences difficulty or frustration, stop. Try to make your sessions brief and positive. If you want to further enrich your child's speech program and language development, you might consider checking out any of the following books from the library and reading them with your child. They contain final /r/ in the titles.

Brown Bear, Brown Bear, What Do You See? by Eric Carle
Goldilocks and the Three Bears by James Marshall
Imogene's Antlers by David Small
The Very Hungry Caterpillar by Eric Carle
What Do You Do, Dear? by Sesyle Joslin
Where Does the Brown Bear Go? by Nicki Weiss

Songs you can sing emphasizing final /r/ are "Farmer in the Dell," "Twinkle, Twinkle Little Star," "Where, Oh Where Has My Little Dog Gone?" and "Row, Row, Row Your Boat."

Thank you for your support. Please sign and return this when you have completed the above lessons.

Additional Teacher Comment *(optional):*

Parent signature _____

Please write your comments, if any, on the other side of this memo.

GRR VAMPIRE ACTIVITY PAGE

Color the pictures that end in /r/.

©1996 by Elizabeth Krepelin and Bonnie Mae Smith

146

GRR VAMPIRE PUPPET PATTERNS

GRR VAMPIRE PUPPET PATTERN

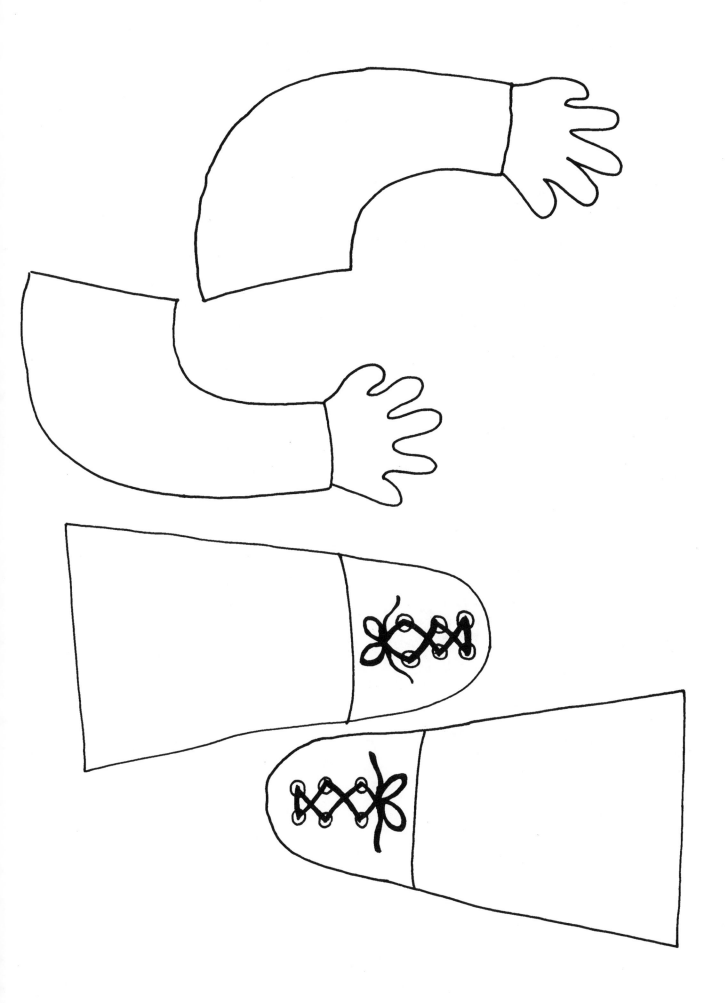

GRR VAMPIRE B&W FLANNEL BOARD FIGURES

45

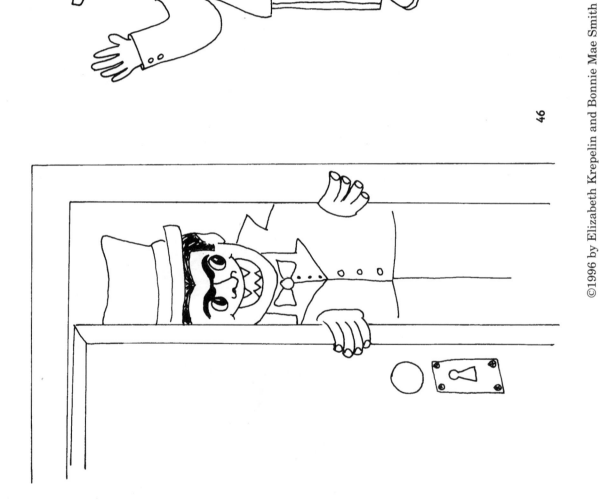

46

CUTE CAT

FLANNEL BOARD STORY

My cat is the cutest pet on the street. *(figure 47)* In fact, his name is Cute. He has white feet, but the rest of his coat is rust. He has great eyes the color of grapefruit. His best playmate is a parrot named Peanut. *(figure 48)* Cute has a habit of going out to hunt late at night. He once caught a rat. But don't fret! He won't bite you! He's sweet and, most important, he's quite cute!

CUTE CAT SONG

(Can be sung to "Twinkle, Twinkle Little Star")

Cute Cat, Cute Cat is my pet.
He's the best cat you have met.

His fur is rust, his eyes quite yellow.
He's a purry, sweet, fat fellow.

Cute Cat, Cute Cat is my pet.
He's the best cat you have met.

VOCABULARY

Final /t/

ONE-SYLLABLE WORDS

bat	cheat	get	knot	right	swat
beat	coat	goat	late	scout	sweet
bet	cute	great	light	seat	tight
bite	date	greet	night	shout	treat
blot	eight	hat	note	sit	trot
boat	fat	heat	nut	skate	vote
boot	flat	hit	out	split	wait
brought	foot	hoot	pet	spot	wet
bright	fret	hot	plate	state	what
cat	fruit	jet	quit	straight	white
caught	gate	kite	rat	street	yet

TWO-SYLLABLE WORDS

about	combat	exit	locket	rabbit
basket	compute	faucet	market	robot
bonnet	create	forget	parrot	rocket
bracelet	donate	habit	peanut	upset
closet	doughnut	jacket	quiet	without

CUTE CAT PUPPET

Materials:

orange construction paper;

black marker or crayon;

oil pastels in yellow, white, peach, or the same
   colors in tempera paint and three cotton swabs;

lunch bag;

scissors;

glue

Directions:

1. Duplicate the patterns on construction paper. Cut off one inch from the bottom of the bag.

2. Trace the cat with black marker or crayon. Fill in the eyeliner, pupil of the eye, and nostrils with black. Draw on whiskers. Color the eyes yellow, using either oil pastel or cotton swab with tempera paint. Color or paint the triangular tip of the nose peach. Color or paint the feet white.

3. Cut out the pieces and glue to the bag, being careful to line up the mouth.

PARENT MEMO

Today's date: _____

Child's name: _____

Dear Parent:

Please set aside five minutes a day to work on these exercises for final /t/.

Please read these words to your child every day. Your child is to listen, but not repeat them to you.

beat	doughnut	jet	rocket	skate
bite	flat	knot	scout	split
bright	fruit	note	shout	trout

Your child should practice saying these each day. Check off each time he or she says the words to you.

bat
0 0 0 0 0

boot
0 0 0 0 0

cat
0 0 0 0 0

eight
0 0 0 0 0

kite
0 0 0 0 0

rat
0 0 0 0 0

Helping your child with speech homework will be an important advantage for your child's progress. If your child experiences difficulty or frustration, stop. Try to make your sessions brief and positive. If you want to further enrich your child's speech program and language development, you might consider checking out any of the following books from the library and reading them with your child. They contain final /t/ in the titles.

Eating the Alphabet by Lois Ehlert
Little Toot by Hardie Gramatky
The Cat in the Hat by Dr. Seuss
The Velveteen Rabbit by Margery Williams
"This Little Piggy Went to Market," Mother Goose
Who Took the Farmer's Hat? by Joan L. Nodset

Songs you can sing emphasizing final /t/ are "Oh Dear, What Can the Matter Be?" "Mexican Hat Dance," and "There's a Hole in the Bucket."

Thank you for your support. Please sign and return this when you have completed the above lessons.

Additional Teacher Comment *(optional):*

Parent signature _____

Please write your comments, if any, on the back of this memo.

CUTE CAT ACTIVITY PAGE

Color the pictures that end in /t/. Some are hidden in the tree!

154

CUTE CAT PUPPET PATTERN

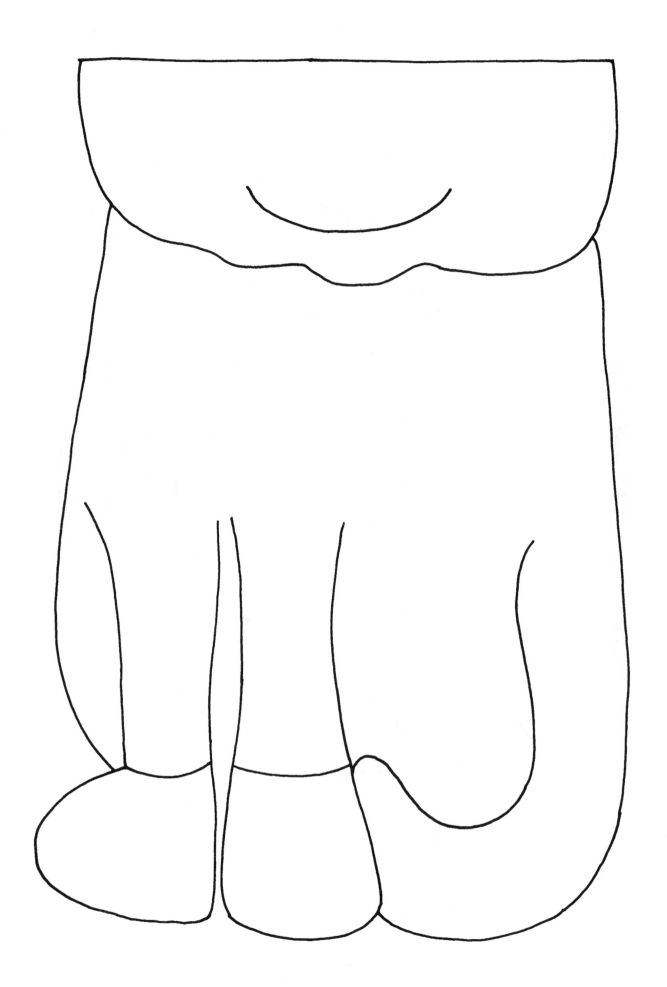

CUTE CAT B&W FLANNEL BOARD FIGURE

48

47

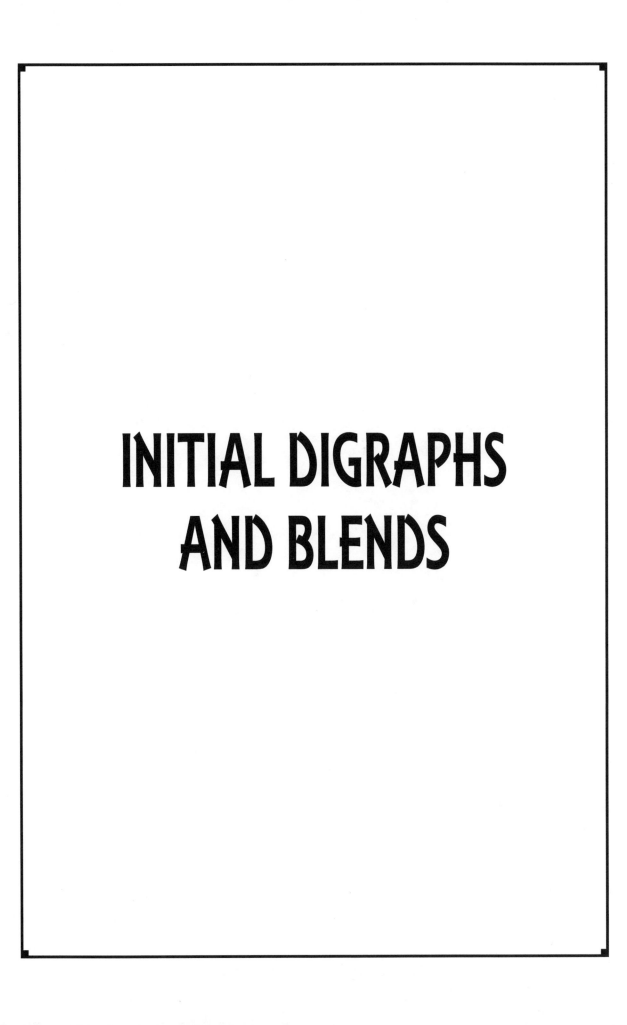

INITIAL DIGRAPHS
AND BLENDS

BLUE BLOODHOUND

FLANNEL BOARD STORY

Blue Bloodhound lives near a blackberry bush in Blue Bluff. *(figure 49)* His owner, Blanton Black, is a blinky, blond, bland bloke. You can't blame Blue if he lies on his blanket and bleats, "Blah!"

Bliss to him would be to blast out in a blaze for the hunt. To be blatantly blunt, Blue's life is too bland for a blossoming bloodhound. In order to blossom and not be a blob, he needs to get away from Blanton Black.

BLUE BLOODHOUND SONG

(Can be sung to "The Farmer in the Dell")

Blue needs to bloom.
Blue needs to bloom.
In a blissful blaze
To spend his days,
Blue needs to bloom.

VOCABULARY

Initial /bl/

ONE-SYLLABLE WORDS

blab	blast	blend	blitz	blotch
black	blaze	bless	blob	blouse
blade	bleach	blimp	block	blow
blame	bleak	blind	blood	blue
bland	bleat	blink	bloom	blur
blank	bleed	bliss	blot	blush
blare				

TWO-SYLLABLE WORDS

blacksmith	blarney	blizzard	blubber	blunder
blacktop	blister	blossom	bluebird	bluster
blanket				

BLUE BLOODHOUND PUPPET

Materials:

brown paper;

red, black, and yellow crayons;

lunch bag;

scissors;

glue

Directions:

1. Duplicate the patterns on construction paper. Cut off one inch from the bottom of the bag.

2. Outline with black. Fill in the eyes and nose with black. Fill in the collar with red. Fill in license and buckle with yellow.

3. Cut out. Glue on head. Line up flat part with the edge of the flap. Ears hang down. Line up the body with the mouth, and glue.

PARENT MEMO

Today's date: _____

Child's name: _____

Dear Parent:

Please set aside five minutes a day to work on these exercises for initial /bl/.

Please read these words to your child every day. Your child is to listen, but not repeat them to you.

black	blast	bless	blitz	blue
blank	bleach	blind	bloom	blur
blanket	blend	blink	blossom	blush

Your child should practice saying these each day. Check off each time he or she says the words to you.

blade
0 0 0 0 0

blanket
0 0 0 0 0

bleach
0 0 0 0 0

blimp
0 0 0 0 0

block
0 0 0 0 0

blouse
0 0 0 0 0

Helping your child with speech homework will be an important advantage for your child's progress. If your child experiences difficulty or frustration, stop. Try to make your sessions brief and positive. If you want to further enrich your child's speech program and language development, you might consider checking out any of the following books from the library and reading them with your child. They contain initial /bl/ in the titles.

Leo the Late Bloomer by Robert Kraus
"Little Boy Blue," Mother Goose
Old Black Fly by Jim Aylesworth
The Blanket by Margot Apple

A song you can sing emphasizing initial /bl/ is "Three Blind Mice."

Thank you for your support. Please sign and return this when you have completed the above lessons.

Additional Teacher Comment *(optional):*

Parent signature _____

Please write your comments, if any, on the back of this memo.

BLUE BLOODHOUND ACTIVITY PAGE

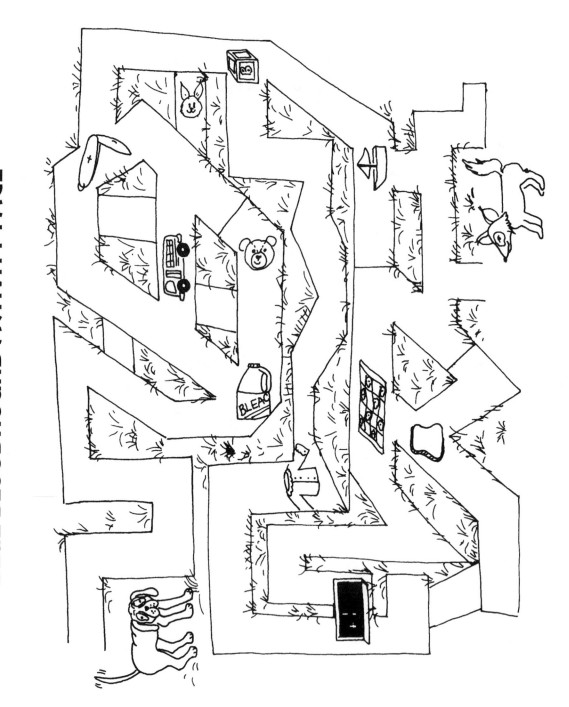

Color the pictures that begin with /bl/ to help Blue find his way to a friend.

©1996 by Elizabeth Krepelin and Bonnie Mae Smith

BLUE BLOODHOUND PUPPET PATTERN

BLUE BLOODHOUND B&W FLANNEL BOARD FIGURE

49

CHUBBS CHICKEN

FLANNEL BOARD STORY

Chubbs Chicken lives in a church yard in Chattanooga. *(figure 50)* Chubbs is chubby because she eats Cheerios™, Cheetos™, cheddar cheese, and chocolate chips. She sometimes eats cherries, chowder or chili, just for a change.

Chubbs cheers for all champions and chortles and chuckles at choice jokes. Her husband, Chuck, thinks Chubbs is charming. Their children cheep their agreement every chance they get. *(figure 51)* This makes Chubbs quite cheerful and keeps her chugging along.

CHUBBS CHICKEN SONG

(Can be sung to "I'm Brining Home a Baby Bumblebee")

Charming Chubbs Chicken, don't you see?
Chowder, chips, and chocolate aren't fat free!
They'll change you to a chubby chickadee!
Here! Have some celery—charged to me!

VOCABULARY

Initial /ch/

ONE-SYLLABLE WORDS

chain	charm	cheer	chime	chose
chair	chat	cheese	chin	chug
chalk	cheap	chess	chip	chum
champ	cheat	chew	chirp	chunk
chance	check	chick	choice	church
change	cheek	child	choke	
charge	cheep	chill	chop	

TWO-SYLLABLE WORDS

cello	checkers	chicken	chirrup	chowmein
challenge	cheerful	chili	chitchat	chubby
channel	cherish	chimney	choosy	chuckle
chapter	cherry	china	chortle	
chatter	cherub	chipmunk	chowder	

CHUBBS CHICKEN PUPPET

Materials:

yellow and orange construction paper;

black crayon;

lunch bag;

scissors;

glue

Directions:

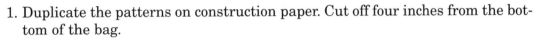

1. Duplicate the patterns on construction paper. Cut off four inches from the bottom of the bag.

2. Outline all parts with black. Cut out all parts.

3. Glue on top of the head. Put on beak; it hangs over a bit. Glue on bottom part of puppet. Glue on bottom of beak so it matches up to top. Glue on feet. Draw on eyes with black.

PARENT MEMO

Today's date: _____

Child's name: _____

Dear Parent:

Please set aside five minutes a day to work on these exercises for initial /ch/.

Please read these words to your child every day. Your child is to listen, but not repeat them to you.

chain	chance	chat	cherish	choice
chalk	charge	cheer	chime	chug
champ	charm	cheese	chin	church

Your child should practice saying these each day. Check off each time he or she says the words to you.

chain
O O O O O

chair
O O O O O

check
O O O O O

cheese
O O O O O

chick
O O O O O

church
O O O O O

Helping your child with speech homework will be an important advantage for your child's progress. If your child experiences difficulty or frustration, stop. Try to make your sessions brief and positive. If you want to further enrich your child's speech program and language development, you might consider checking out any of the following books from the library and reading them with your child. They contain initial /ch/ in the titles.

Chickens Aren't the Only Ones by Ruth Heller
Chicka Chicka Boom Boom by Bill Martin, Jr. and John Archambault
Chicken Little (any version)
"Here's the Church, Here's the Steeple" (a finger play)
Peter's Chair by Ezra J. Keats

Thank you for your support. Please sign and return this when you have completed the above lessons.

Additional Teacher Comment *(optional):*

Parent signature _____

Please write your comments, if any, on the back of this memo.

CHUBBS CHICKEN ACTIVITY PAGE

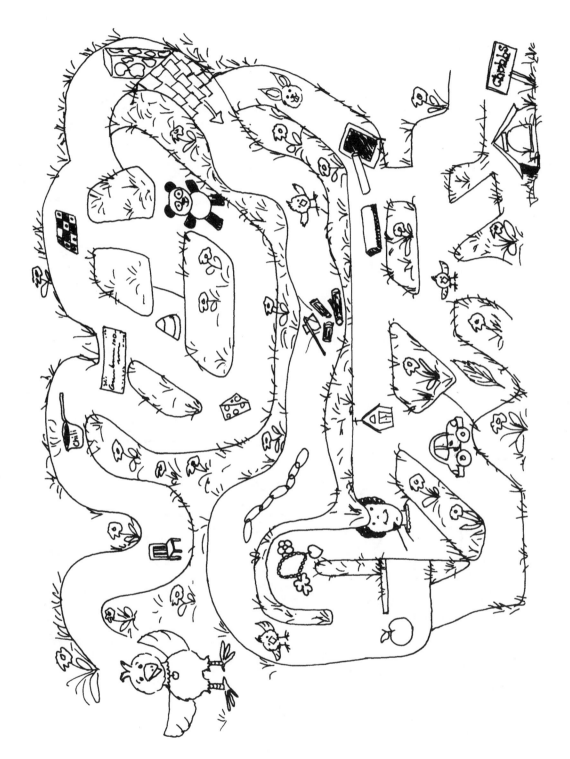

Color the pictures that begin with /ch/ to help Chubbs find the path home.

171

CHUBBS CHICKEN PUPPET PATTERNS

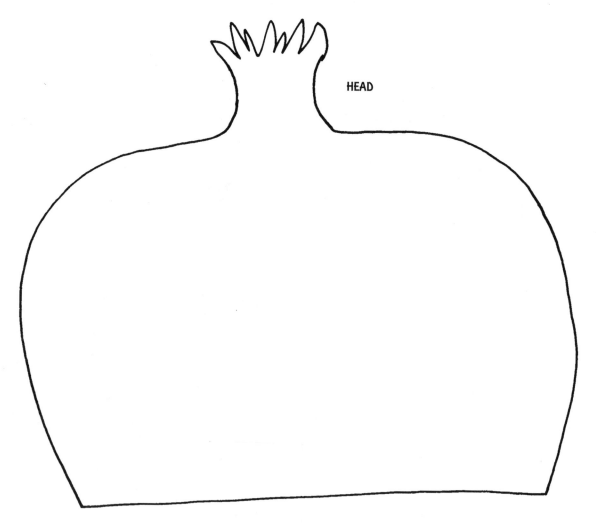

HEAD

BEAK BOTOM

BEAK TOP

LEGS

CHUBBS CHICKEN PUPPET PATTERN

YELLOW BODY

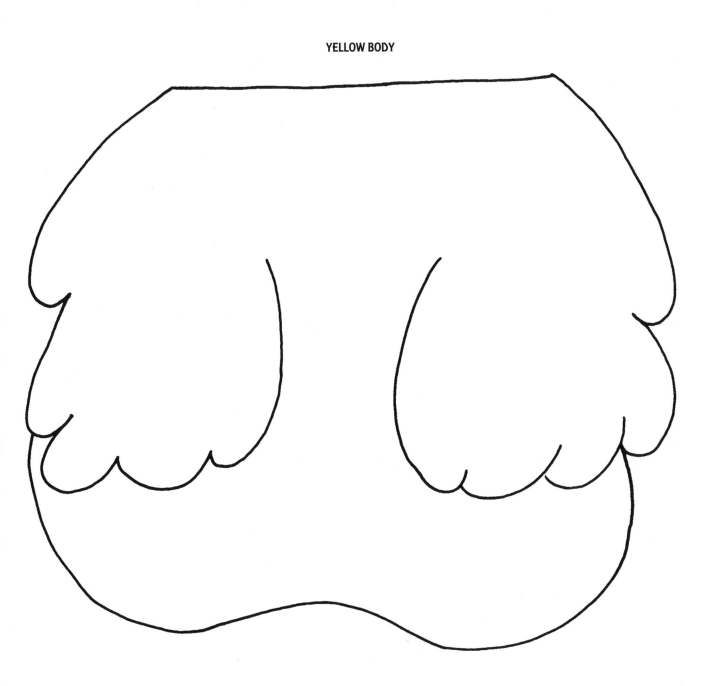

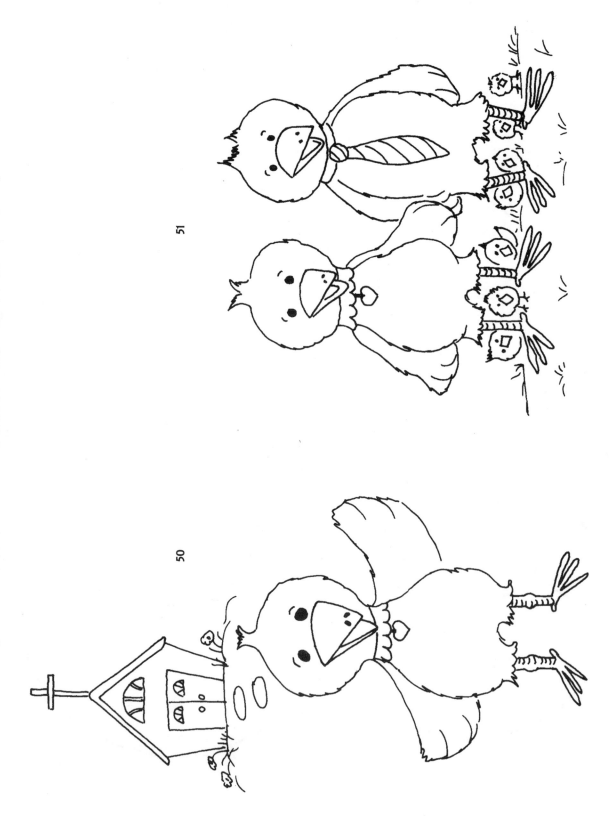

50

51

CLEO CLOWN

FLANNEL BOARD STORY

Cleo Clown was a clerk until he got a clue and joined the circus to claim fame. He clad himself in clown clothes *(figure 52)* He would clang a bell, climb a cloud, and cluck at clams. He would clutch a clock and act clumsy. *(figure 53)*

It was clear the crowds loved Cleo because they would clamor and clap for more. Cleo was such a clever clown that he was asked to teach a class!

CLEO CLOWN SONG

(Can be sung to "Smoky the Bear" chorus)

Cleo Clown, Cleo Clown,
Cleverest fellow anywhere around.
He can make you laugh before you clap a hand.
Claims to be the best clown in the whole entire land.
(repeat)

VOCABULARY

Initial /kl/

ONE-SYLLABLE WORDS

clack	claw	click	clock	club
claim	clay	cliff	clod	cluck
clam	clean	climb	clop	clue
clap	clear	clip	clothes	clutch
clash	clerk	cloak	cloud	klutz
class				

TWO-SYLLABLE WORDS

clackers	cleanly	climate	closet	clubhouse
clamor	clearance	clinic	clothespin	clumsy
classic	clergy	clipboard	cloudy	cluster
classmate	clever	clobber	clover	clutter
classroom	client			

CLEO CLOWN PUPPET

Materials:

yellow, orange, white, and red construction paper;

Overwriter™ markers *(optional);*

markers or crayons;

colored yarn for hair *(optional);*

lunch bag;

scissors;

glue

Directions:

1. Duplicate the patterns on construction paper. Cut off one inch from the bottom of the bag.

2. Color in triangles over eyes black. Outline eyes, hat, suit, shoes, and gloves with black. Color nose and top and bottom lips red. Color inside of mouth with black. Color hatband black. Decorate hat and suit as desired. Overwriter markers make interesting designs for the suit.

3. Cut pieces of yarn and glue on for sides for hair, or use orange construction paper pattern hair. Glue on clown top of head. Glue on clown suit. Glue on bottom of face, centered to match up with top. Glue on hair, hat, gloves, and shoes.

PARENT MEMO

Today's date: _____

Child's name: _____

Dear Parent:

Please set aside five minutes a day to work on these exercises for initial /kl/.

Please read these words to your child every day. Your child is to listen, but not repeat them to you.

claim	class	clean	clod	cluck
clap	claw	clever	closet	clue
clash	clay	cloak	clothes	clutch

Your child should practice saying these each day. Check off each time he or she says the words to you.

clam
0 0 0 0 0

clip
0 0 0 0 0

clock
0 0 0 0 0

cloud
0 0 0 0 0

clown
0 0 0 0 0

club
0 0 0 0 0

Helping your child with speech homework will be an important advantage for your child's progress. If your child experiences difficulty or frustration, stop. Try to make your sessions brief and positive. If you want to further enrich your child's speech program and language development, you might consider checking out any of the following books from the library and reading them with your child. They contain initial /kl/ in the titles.

Clown of God by Tomie DePaola
The Cloud Book by Tomie DePaola
There's a Nightmare in My Closet by Mercer Mayer

Thank you for your support. Please sign and return this when you have completed the above lessons.

Additional Teacher Comment *(optional):*

Parent signature _____

Please write your comments, if any, on the back of this memo.

CLEO CLOWN ACTIVITY PAGE

Color the pictures that begin with /cl/.

©1996 by Elizabeth Krepelin and Bonnie Mae Smith

CLEO CLOWN PUPPET PATTERNS

CLEO CLOWN PUPPET PATTERNS

RED

TWO ORANGE HAIR PIECES

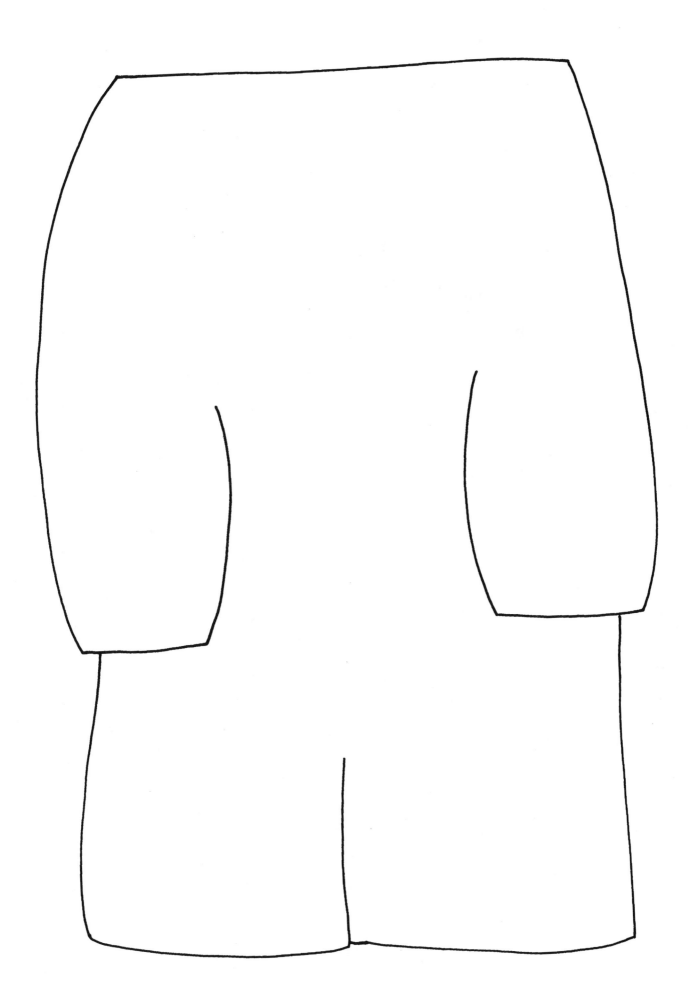

53

52

CRAZY CROW

FLANNEL BOARD STORY

Crazy Crow is a critter who lives near a corn crib in Crayfish Creek. *(figure 54)* He creates a crisis for Farmer Crosby when he craftily crashes into his crop and crudely crusades to crack his corn. *(figure 55)* Crazy is a crook who makes Crosby cry and want to crack that creature on the cranium.

CRAZY COW SONG

(Can be sung to "It's Raining, It's Pouring")

I'm craftily amazing.
The other crows are praising.
I eat crack corn
I'm the best thief born.
I drive Farmer Crosby crazy.
Crazy Crow is my name.
Stealing corn is my game.

VOCABULARY

Initial /kr/

ONE-SYLLABLE WORDS

chrome	crate	creep	crop	cruise
crab	crave	crew	cross	crumb
craft	crawl	crib	crow	crunch
cram	creak	crime	crowd	crush
cramp	cream	crisp	crown	crust
crank	crease	croak	crude	cry
crash	creek			

TWO-SYLLABLE WORDS

crabby	crayon	credit	crimson	crusade
cracker	crazy	creepy	crumble	crystal
cradle	create	cricket		

CRAZY CROW PUPPET

Materials:

black and orange construction paper;

2 hole reinforcers;

black crayon or marker;

carbon paper *(optional);*

lunch bag;

scissors;

glue

Directions:

1. Duplicate the patterns on construction paper. Cut off three inches from the bottom of the bag.

2. Trace the body and wings onto black paper using carbon paper or a pattern. Outline beak and legs with black.

3. Cut out all parts. Glue on the head, lining up the bottom flat edge with the top flap of the paper bag. Glue on the top of the beak. It hangs over the edge. Put hole reinforcer eyes on head. Glue on the body. Glue legs to the body. Line up the bottom part of the beak to the top. Glue on wings.

PARENT MEMO

Today's date: _____

Child's name: _____

Dear Parent:

Please set aside five minutes a day to work on these exercises for initial /kr/.

Please read these words to your child every day. Your child is to listen, but not repeat them to you.

craft	creak	creep	crisp	crowd
crave	cream	crew	croak	crown
crawl	creek	crime	cross	crush

Your child should practice saying these each day. Check off each time he or she says the words to you.

crab
O O O O O

crib
O O O O O

cross
O O O O O

crow
O O O O O

crown
O O O O O

cry
O O O O O

Helping your child with speech homework will be an important advantage for your child's progress. If your child experiences difficulty or frustration, stop. Try to make your sessions brief and positive. If you want to further enrich your child's speech program and language development, you might consider checking out any of the following books from the library and reading them with your child. They contain initial /kr/ in the titles.

A House for Hermit Crab by Eric Carle
Cranberry Thanksgiving by Wende Devlin and Harry Devlin
Harold and the Purple Crayon by Crockett Johnson
The Very Quiet Cricket by Eric Carle

A song you can sing emphasizing initial /kr/ is "Jimmy Crack Corn."

Thank you for your support. Please sign and return this when you have completed the above lessons.

Additional Teacher Comment *(optional):*

Parent signature _____

Please write your comments, if any, on the back of this memo.

CRAZY CROW ACTIVITY PAGE

Color the hidden pictures that begin with /cr/.

©1996 by Elizabeth Krepelin and Bonnie Mae Smith

CRAZY CROW PUPPET PATTERNS

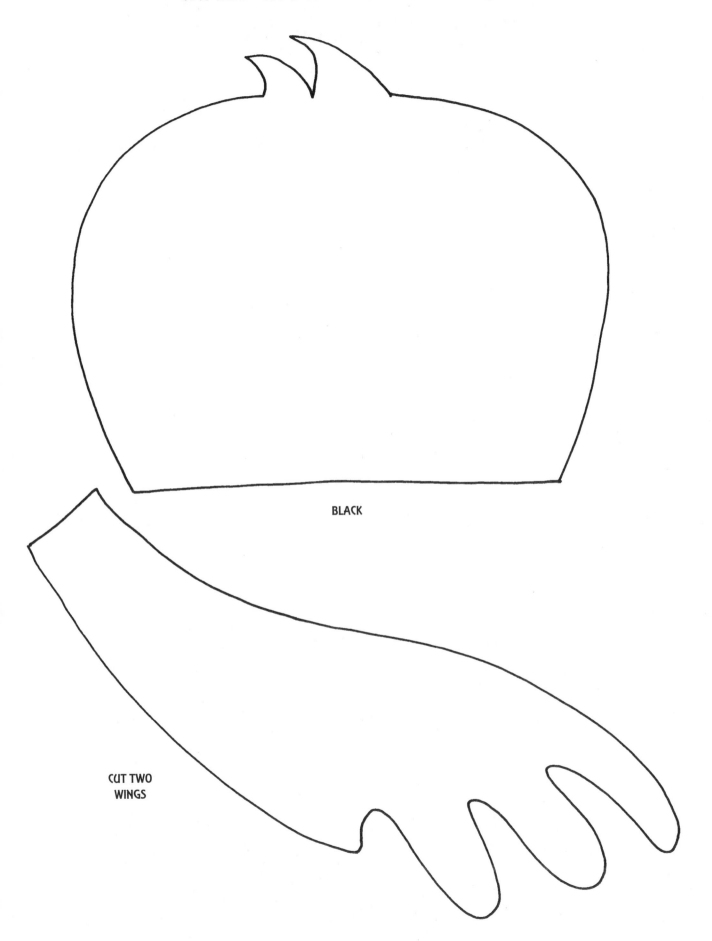

BLACK

CUT TWO
WINGS

CRAZY CROW PUPPET PATTERN

BLACK

CRAZY CROW PUPPET PATTERNS

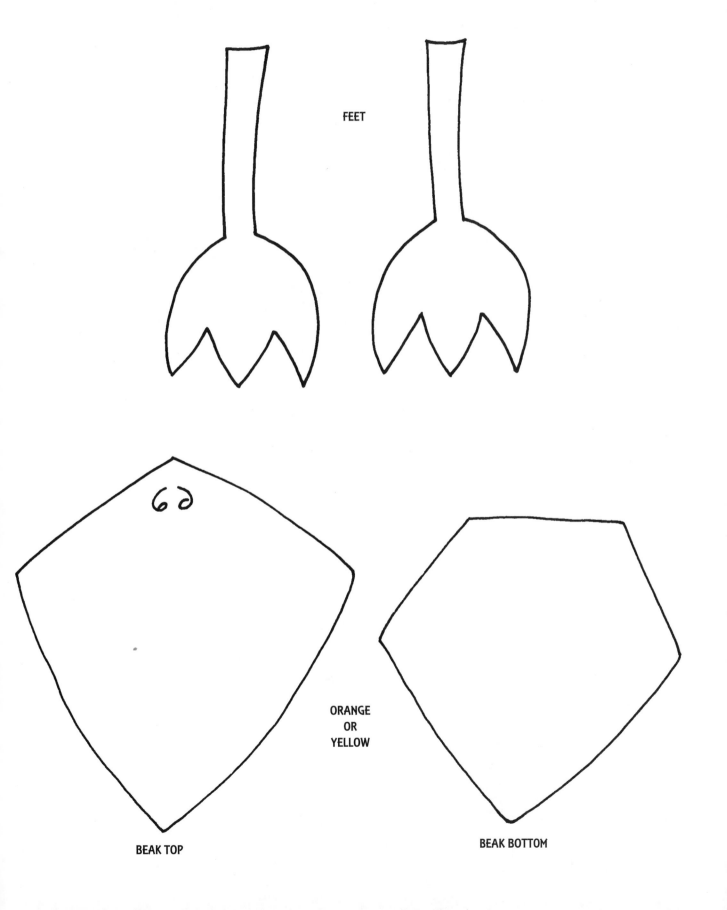

FEET

ORANGE
OR
YELLOW

BEAK TOP

BEAK BOTTOM

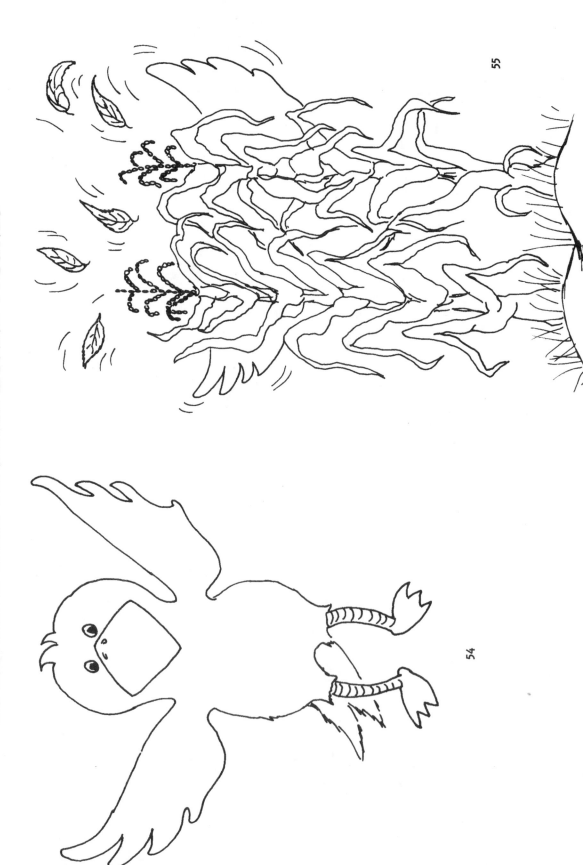

55

54

DRU DRAGON

FLANNEL BOARD STORY

Dru Dragon was part of a drama many years ago in Dryville *(figure 56)*. There was a dreaded drought in Dryville. That means there was not a drop to drink. The plants were drab.

Dru always had a cloud over his head. When he dragged into town, his cloud dropped a drizzle, a drip, and then a driving rain on the town. *(figure 57)* There was so much rain, the people got drenched and dreaded drowning. Since Dru was only passing through and didn't stay to dream, he solved the drought and the town was renamed Druville.

DRU DRAGON SONG

(Can be sung to "Turn the Glasses Over")

Dru Dragon, Dru Dragon, with cloud hanging over.
Please come to Dryville and pass over.
Come solve the drought
All the people will shout,
"Make the name of our town Druville."

Come drip soon, night or noon,
Come drip water on Dryville.
Please solve the drought
All the people will shout,
"Make the name of our town Druville."

VOCABULARY

Initial /dr/

ONE-SYLLABLE WORDS

drab	draw	drift	drool	drudge
draft	dread	drill	droop	drug
drag	dream	drink	drop	drum
drain	drench	drip	drove	drunk
drank	dress	drive	drown	dry
drape	drew	droll	drowse	

TWO-SYLLABLE WORDS

drafty	drawer	dressy	driveway	droplet
<u>dragon</u>	dreadful	dribble	<u>drizzle</u>	drumstick
drama	dreamer	driver	droopy	dryer
drastic	dreary			

DRU DRAGON PUPPET

Materials:

lavender construction paper;

green, white, and orange crayons;

lunch bag;

scissors;

glue

Directions:

1. Duplicate the patterns on construction paper. Cut off three inches from the bottom of the bag.

2. Outline all body parts in green. Fill in eyelid, top of wings, nose, and tummy stripes with solid green. Fill in teeth and nails with white. Color in topknot and inside of mouth with orange.

3. Cut out all parts. Glue on top of head. Glue on bottom part of body. Glue wings on back of bag.

PARENT MEMO

Today's date: _____

Child's name: _____

Dear Parent:

Please set aside five minutes a day to work on these exercises for initial /dr/.

Please read these words to your child every day. Your child is to listen, but not repeat them to you.

drag	draw	drew	drip	drop
dragon	dream	drift	drizzle	drug
drain	drench	drink	drool	dry

Your child should practice saying these each day. Check off each time he or she says the words to you.

dragon
0 0 0 0 0

dress
0 0 0 0 0

drill
0 0 0 0 0

drink
0 0 0 0 0

drip
0 0 0 0 0

drum
0 0 0 0 0

Helping your child with speech homework will be an important advantage for your child's progress. If your child experiences difficulty or frustration, stop. Try to make your sessions brief and positive. If you want to further enrich your child's speech program and language development, you might consider checking out any of the following books from the library and reading them with your child. They contain initial /dr/ in the titles.

Dragons by Eric Carle
Drummer Hoff by Barbara Emberley
Mary Wore Her Red Dress, and Henry Wore His Green Sneakers by Merle Peek
My Father's Dragon by Ruth S. Gannett

Songs you can sing emphasizing initial /dr/ are "Little Drummer Boy" and "Puff the Magic Dragon."

Thank you for your support. Please sign and return this when you have completed the above lessons.

Additional Teacher Comment *(optional):*

Parent signature _____

Please write your comments, if any, on the back of this memo.

DRU DRAGON ACTIVITY PAGE

Color the pictures that begin with /dr/ to help Dru Dragon find the way to Dryville.

DRU DRAGON PUPPET PATTERN

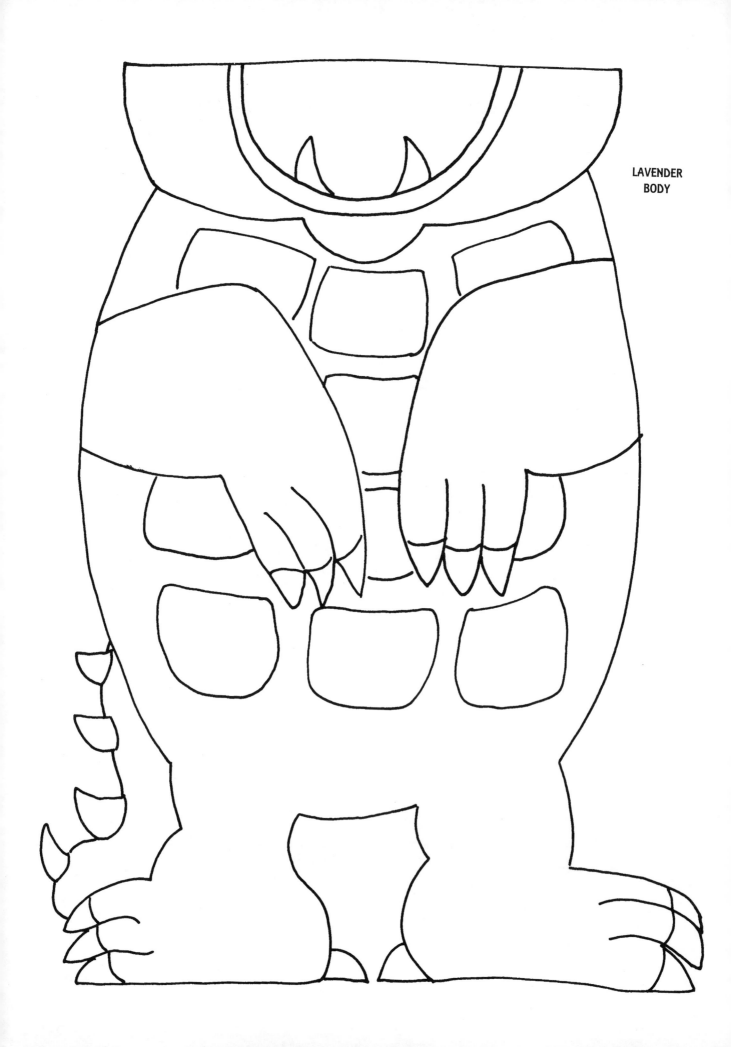

LAVENDER
BODY

DRU DRAGON PUPPET PATTERN

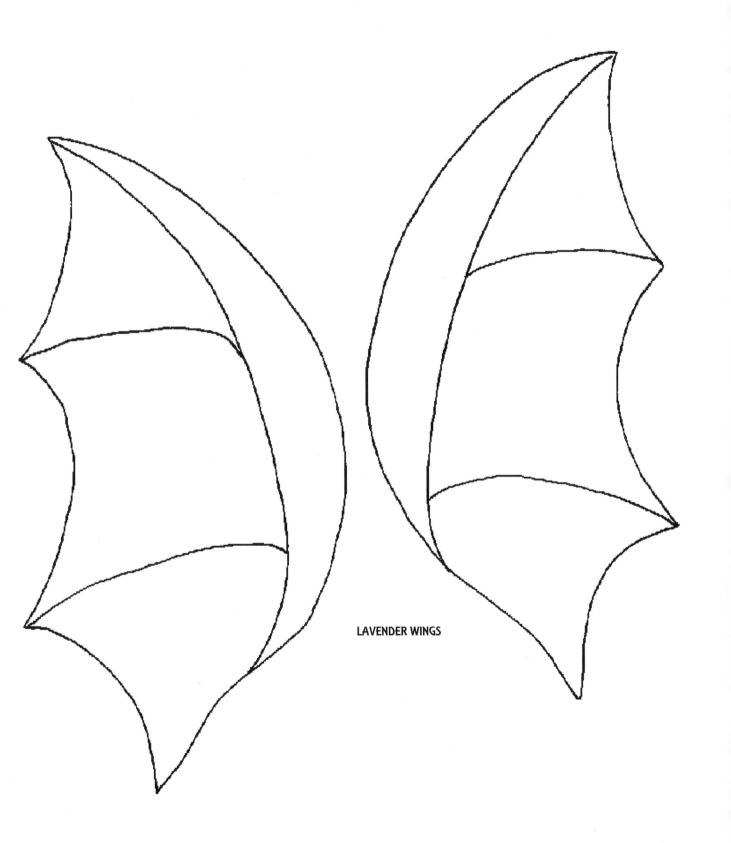

LAVENDER WINGS

DRU DRAGON B&W FLANNEL BOARD FIGURES

57

56

FLIT FLAMINGO

FLANNEL BOARD STORY

Flit Flamingo flourished in a flock in Florida. *(figure 58)* She flipped for flowers, flags, and fluoride flap jacks. Flit's heart flip-flopped and fluttered the day she met Floyd Flamingo. *(figure 59)* She flirted with flair, he flapped his fluorescent wings, and they flew off to live in a flat in Flagstaff.

FLIT FLAMINGO SONG

(Can be sung to "The Ants Go Marching")

Flit Flamingo flirted with Floyd
Hurrah! Hurrah!
Flit Flamingo flirted with Floyd
Hurrah! Hurrah!
Flit Flamingo flirted with Floyd.
Her charms were more than he could avoid.
And they flapped and flew away.
They're together even today.
Flap, flap, flap!

VOCABULARY

Initial /fl/

ONE-SYLLABLE WORDS

flab	flat	flew	float	fluff
flail	flaunt	flick	flock	fluke
flair	flaw	flies	flood	flung
flak	flea	flight	floor	flunk
flake	fleck	flinch	flop	flush
flame	fled	fling	floss	flute
flap	flee	flip	flour	fly
flash	fleet	flirt	flow	
flask	flesh	flit	flu	

TWO-SYLLABLE WORDS

flabby	flannel	fleecy	flitter	flounder
flagman	flapper	flicker	floppy	flower
flagpole	flashy	flimsy	floral	<u>fluid</u>
flaming	<u>flavor</u>	flipper	florist	fluster

FLIT FLAMINGO PUPPET

Materials:

light pink and shocking pink construction paper;

black and white crayons;

lunch bag;

scissors;

glue

Directions:

1. Duplicate the patterns on construction paper. Cut off one inch from the bottom of the bag.

2. Outline all parts in black. Fill in bottom part of beak and accent feathers with black and white, coloring hard.

3. Cut out all parts. Glue on head. Neck goes on the far right edge of the top flap of the bag. Glue on body. Glue on the legs and under part of beak, lining up so it matches the top part.

PARENT MEMO

Today's date: _____

Child's name: _____

Dear Parent:

Please set aside five minutes a day to work on these exercises for initial /fl/.

Please read these words to your child every day. Your child is to listen, but not repeat them to you.

flair	flaunt	flit	flood	fluid
flake	flavor	float	floss	flush
flash	flea	flock	fluff	flute

Your child should practice saying these each day. Check off each time he or she says the words to you.

flake
0 0 0 0 0

flame
0 0 0 0 0

flat
0 0 0 0 0

floor
0 0 0 0 0

flower
0 0 0 0 0

fly
0 0 0 0 0

Helping your child with speech homework will be an important advantage for your child's progress. If your child experiences difficulty or frustration, stop. Try to make your sessions brief and positive. If you want to further enrich your child's speech program and language development, you might consider checking out the following book from the library and reading it with your child. It contains initial /fl/ in the title.

Old Black Fly by Jim Aylesworth

Songs you can sing emphasizing initial /fl/ are "There's a Spider on the Floor," "Shoo Fly," "Old Lady that Swallowed a Fly," and "You're a Grand Old Flag."

Thank you for your support. Please sign and return this when you have completed the above lessons.

Additional Teacher Comment *(optional):*

Parent signature _____

Please write your comments, if any, on the back of this memo.

FLIT FLAMINGO ACTIVITY PAGE

Circle the pictures that begin with /fl/.

FLIT FLAMINGO PUPPET PATTERNS

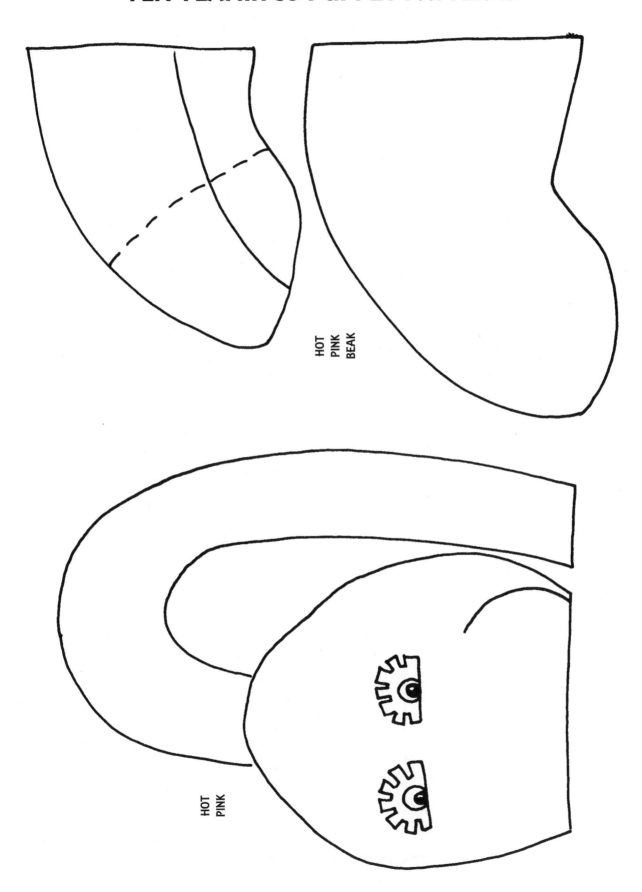

HOT
PINK
BEAK

HOT
PINK

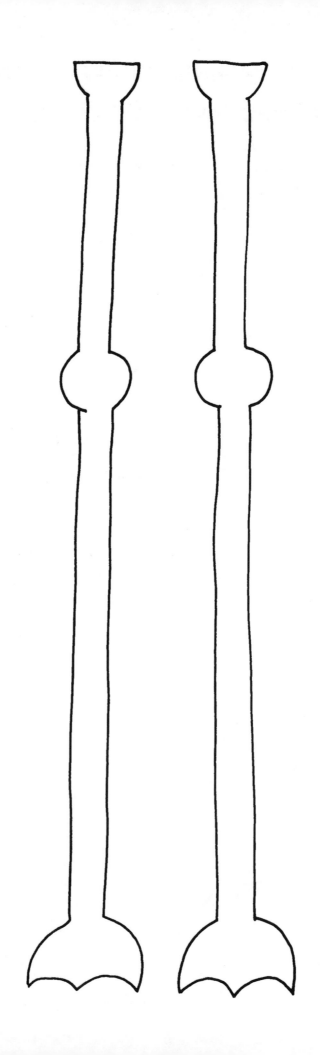

FLIT FLAMINGO PUPPET PATTERN

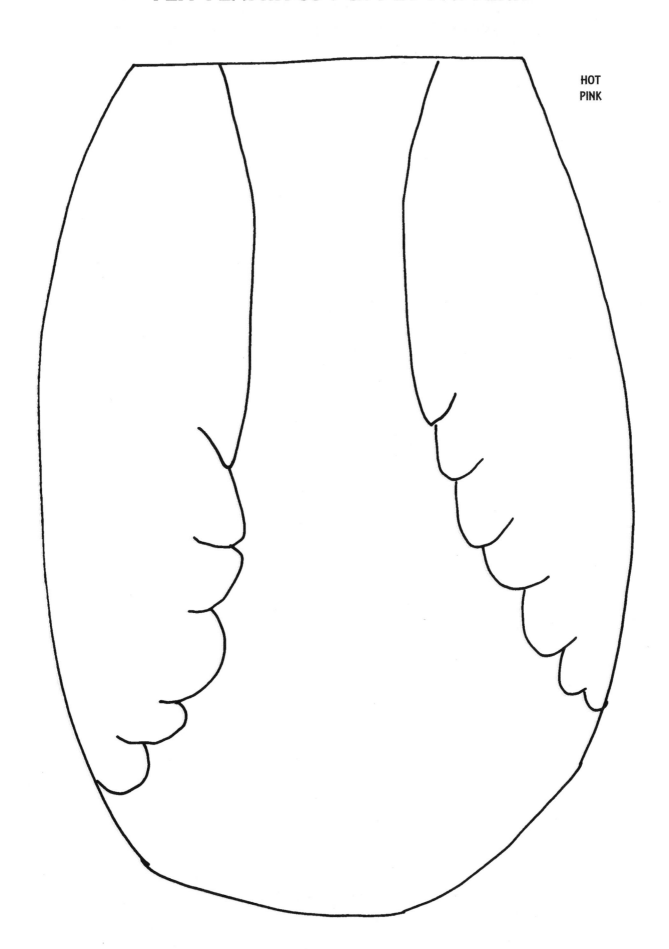

HOT
PINK

FLIT FLAMINGO B&W FLANNEL BOARD FIGURE

©1996 by Elizabeth Krepelin and Bonnie Mae Smith

58

FLIT FLAMINGO B&W FLANNEL BOARD FIGURE

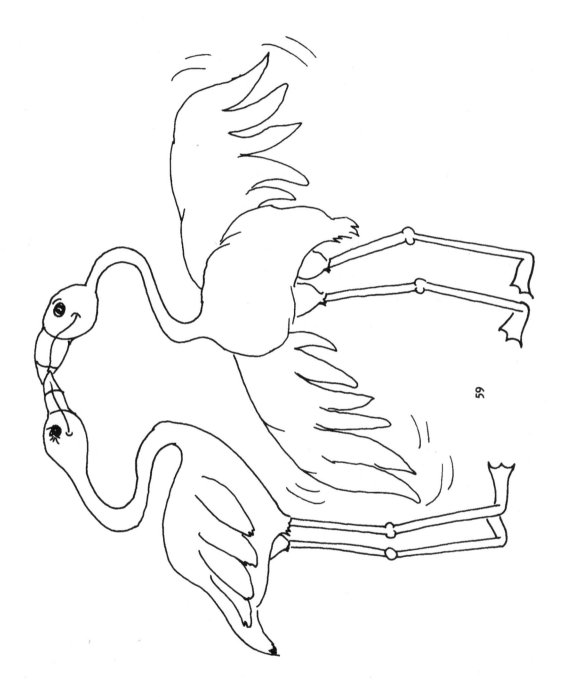

59

FREAKY FRANK

FLANNEL BOARD STORY

Freaky Frank is enough to frighten anyone. *(figure 60)* Frank frequently frets himself to a frazzle because he has no friends. Anyone who sees him frowns, goes into a frenzy, or is frozen with fear. Frank would like a fresh start. He is like the prince frozen in the frog's body. If Frank could get a fresh start, he could be free to frolic and be frisky with a friend.

FREAKY FRANK SONG

(Can be sung to "The Farmer in the Dell")

Frank needs a friend, Frank needs a friend
To laugh and play the live long day,
Frank needs a friend.

VOCABULARY

Initial /fr/

ONE-SYLLABLE WORDS

frail	freeze	friend	frog	frown
frame	freight	fright	from	froze
France	fresh	frill	front	fruit
fray	fret	fringe	frost	fry
freak	fried	frock	froth	phrase
free				

TWO-SYLLABLE WORDS

fraction	freckle	frenzy	frigid	frosting
fracture	freedom	frequent	frisky	frosty
fragile	freestyle	Friday	frizzy	frozen
fragrance	freeway	friendship	frolic	frustrate
frantic	freezer	frighten	frontier	

FREAKY FRANK PUPPET

Materials:

brown and green construction paper;

black, orange, white, and yellow crayons or markers;

lunch bag;

scissors;

glue

Directions:

1. Duplicate the patterns on construction paper. Cut off one inch from the bottom of the bag.

2. Outline entire figure with black. Heavily color hair and eyebrows with orange. Color whites of eyes with white. Color in black for eyes. Color belt and bottom of shoes black. Color in buckle, bolt, and fasteners on shoes with yellow.

3. Cut out all parts. Glue on suit. Glue on top of head. Glue on chin, matching up scar. Glue on hands.

PARENT MEMO

Today's date: _____

Child's name: _____

Dear Parent:

Please set aside five minutes a day to work on these exercises for initial /fr/.

Please read these words to your child every day. Your child is to listen, but not repeat them to you.

fragile	France	freight	friend	front
fragrance	free	fresh	fright	froth
frail	freeze	fret	frill	phrase

Your child should practice saying these each day. Check off each time he or she says the words to you.

frame
0 0 0 0 0

France
0 0 0 0 0

fringe
0 0 0 0 0

frog
0 0 0 0 0

frown
0 0 0 0 0

fruit
0 0 0 0 0

Helping your child with speech homework will be an important advantage for your child's progress. If your child experiences difficulty or frustration, stop. Try to make your sessions brief and positive. If you want to further enrich your child's speech program and language development, you might consider checking out any of the following books from the library and reading them with your child. They contain initial /fr/ in the titles.

Counting on Frank by Rod Clement
Freckle Juice by Judy Blume
Frog and Toad Are Friends by Arnold Lobel
May I Bring a Friend? by Beatrice S. De Regniers

Songs you can sing emphasizing initial /fr/ are "Five Little Speckled Frogs," "Frosty the Snowman," and "Frog Went a Courtin'."

Thank you for your support. Please sign and return this when you have completed the above lessons.

Additional Teacher Comment *(optional):*

Parent signature _____

Please write your comments, if any, on the back of this memo.

FREAKY FRANK ACTIVITY PAGE

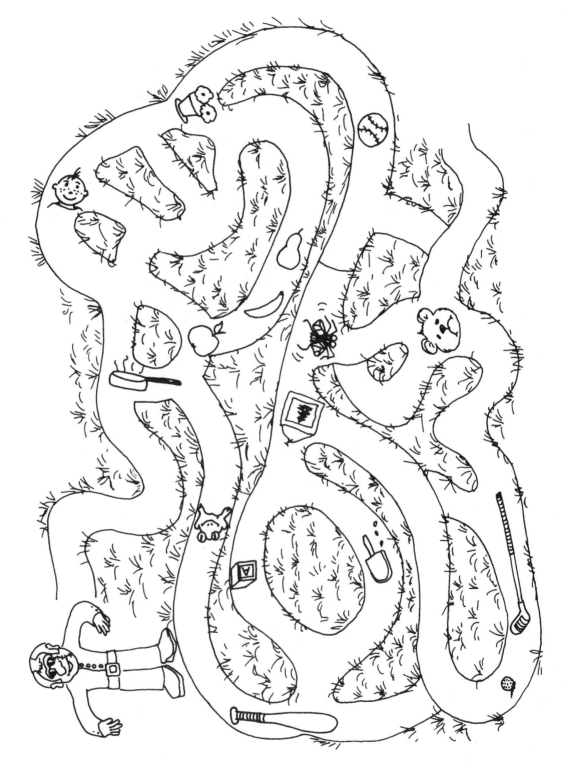

Color the objects that begin with /fr/.

FREAKY FRANK PUPPET PATTERNS

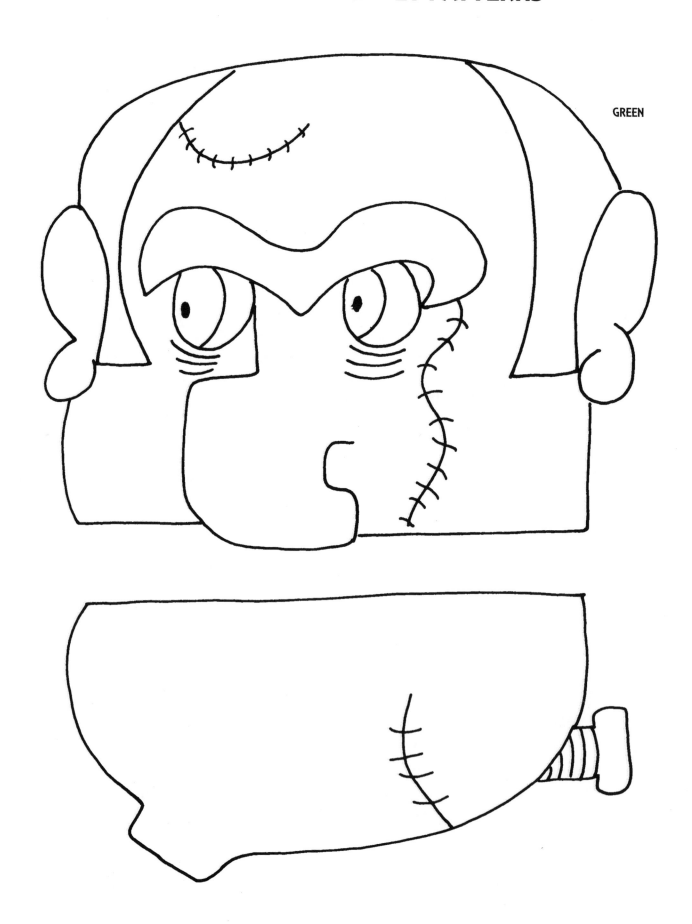

GREEN

FREAKY FRANK PUPPET PATTERN

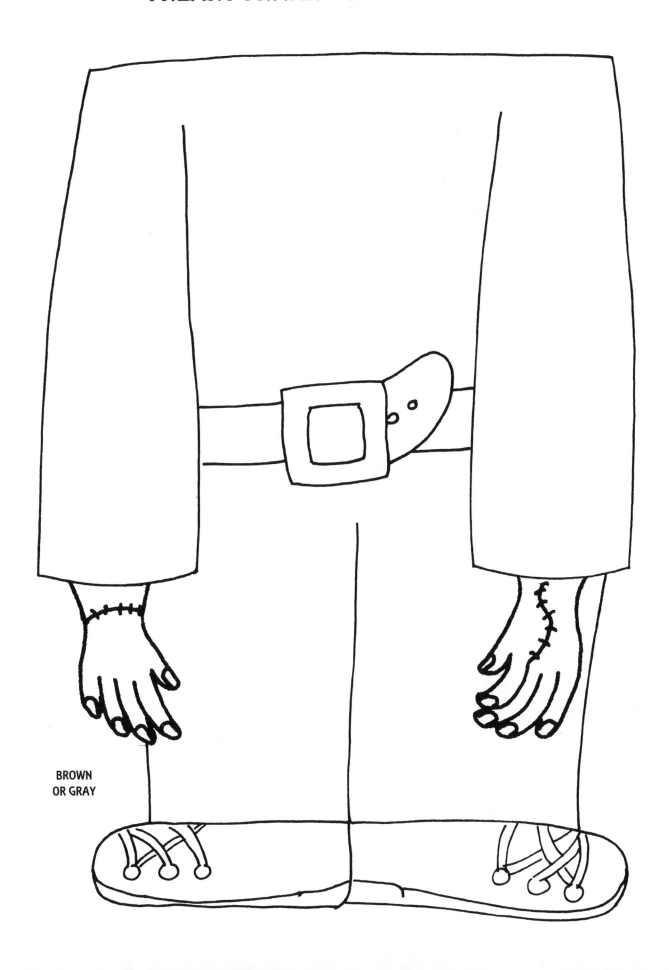

BROWN
OR GRAY

FREAKY FRANK B&W FLANNEL BOARD FIGURE

60

GLOW WORM

FLANNEL BOARD STORY

Glory be! Aren't you glad there is such a thing as a glow worm? *(figure 61)* My friend, Glow, is a glow worm. She lives in Glouster. Glow never glowers or glares and is never gloomy. She doesn't gloat. Glow is glamorous, glossy, glistening, and glowing. She is a glorious worm who is always glad. She glimmers with glee wherever she glides on the globe.

GLOW WORM SONG

(Can be sung to "Battle Hymn of the Republic" chorus)

Glitter, glitter little glow worm.
Glitter, glitter little glow worm.
Glitter, glitter little glow worm.
You gleam and glint with glee.

VOCABULARY

Initial /gl/

ONE-SYLLABLE WORDS

glad	glass	glee	gloat	glove
glade	glaze	glib	globe	glow
glance	gleam	glide	gloom	glue
glare	glean	glimpse	gloss	glum

TWO-SYLLABLE WORDS

glacier	glamour	gleeful	glisten	glory
gladness	glaring	glider	glitter	glossy
Gladys	glasses	glimmer	gloomy	

GLOW WORM PUPPET

Materials:

glitter, any color;

10-mm cup sequin for nose *(optional);*

snowflake sequins for center of eyes *(optional);*

bright yellow and bright blue construction paper;

black and orange crayons;

lunch bag;

scissors;

glue;

cotton swab

Directions:

1. Duplicate the patterns on construction paper. Cut off one inch from the bottom of the bag.

2. Outline face with black. Fill in cheeks and inside of mouth with orange. Cut out all parts. Glue on top of head. Line up body to mouth and glue on. Glue on hat.

3. Using glue and a cotton swab, "paint" strips between worm segments and sprinkle on glitter while the glue is still wet. Do the same to the hatband. Glue on the nose and inside of eyes. Let dry.

PARENT MEMO

Today's date: _____

Child's name: _____

Dear Parent:

Please set aside five minutes a day to work on these exercises for initial /gl/.

Please read these words to your child every day. Your child is to listen, but not repeat them to you.

glacier	glance	glaze	glide	globe
glad	glare	gleam	glimmer	gloom
glamour	glasses	glee	glimpse	glow

Your child should practice saying these each day. Check off each time he or she says the words to you.

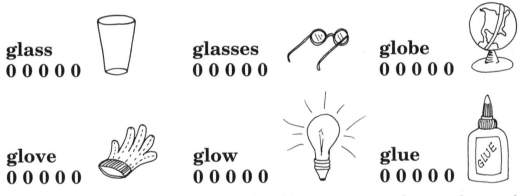

glass
0 0 0 0 0

glasses
0 0 0 0 0

globe
0 0 0 0 0

glove
0 0 0 0 0

glow
0 0 0 0 0

glue
0 0 0 0 0

Helping your child with speech homework will be an important advantage for your child's progress. If your child experiences difficulty or frustration, stop. Try to make your sessions brief and positive. If you want to further enrich your child's speech program and language development, you might consider singing "Turn the Glasses Over" and "Glow Little Glow Worm" with your child. The title and lyrics of these songs emphasize initial /gl/.

Thank you for your support. Please sign and return this when you have completed the above lessons.

Additional Teacher Comment *(optional):*

Parent signature _____

Please write your comments, if any, on the back of this memo.

GLOW WORM ACTIVITY PAGE

Color the pictures that begin with /gl/.

GLOW WORM PUPPET PATTERNS

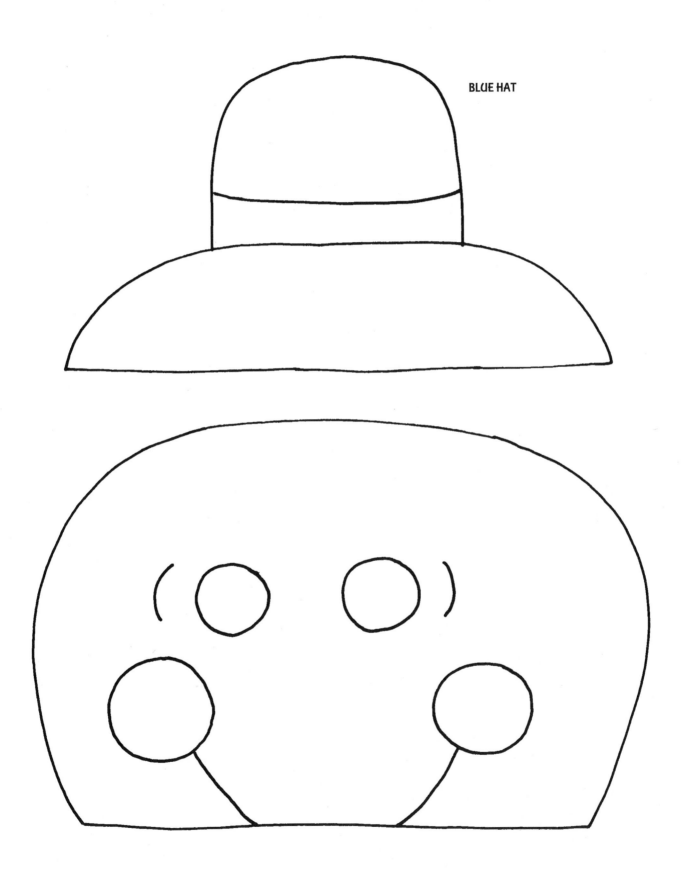

BLUE HAT

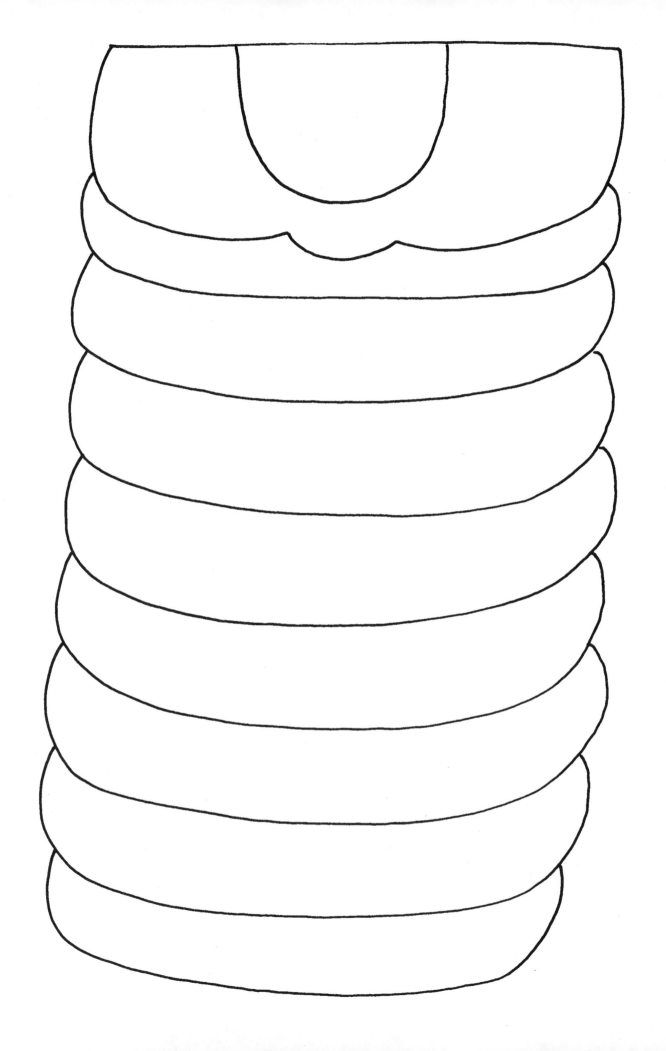

GLOW WORM B&W FLANNEL BOARD FIGURE

61

GRUMPY GRAM

FLANNEL BOARD STORY

Grumpy Gram is grim. *(figure 62)* She grooves on gray grit and grain. She grows her own groceries and grills them, then tops them with green gravy. This tastes so great it makes her grin. *(figure 63)*

Gram is gruff as she grumbles, gropes, groans, gripes, and grasps along the gritty gravel road by her great home near a grove of grapes. She grumbles less when she defies gravity on her broomstick. *(figure 64)*

Gram could grant your wish, but that would be too gracious.

GRUMPY GRAM SONG

(Can be sung to "You're a Grand Old Flag")

Grumpy Gram eats grits
With green gravy on it.
Makes her grumble and grovel and groan.
Makes her grim and mean,
Grouchy and lean,
She won't grant you a wish or a loan.

She jumps on her broom
And flies over the moon,
As a pilot she is no slouch!
You see her grin, don't go for a spin,
Grumpy Gram is a grim old grouch!

VOCABULARY

Initial /gr/

ONE-SYLLABLE WORDS

grab	graph	greet	gripe	grove
grade	grasp	grew	grit	grow
graft	grass	grid	groan	growl
grain	grave	grief	groom	grown
gram	gray	grill	groove	gruff
grand	graze	grim	grouch	grump
grant	great	grin	ground	grunt
grape	green	grind	group	

Two-syllable words

graceful	grandpa	gravel	grimy	gruesome
gracious	granite	greasy	gristle	grumble
grammar	grapefruit	greedy	grizzle	grumpy
grandma	grassy	greeting	groovy	

GRUMPY GRAM PUPPET

Materials:

black, orange, and green construction paper;

carbon paper *(optional);*

black, purple, and green crayons;

lunch bag;

scissors;

glue

Directions:

1. Duplicate the patterns on construction paper.

2. The legs and arms can be left off, depending on the age of the student. Simpler is better for the little ones.

3. With black crayon, color in shoes and stripes on socks, fingernails, inside of mouth, and pupils of eyes. Color eyes green. Color hair and eyelashes purple. Cut out all pieces.

4. Glue on top of head. Her nose and cheeks hang down over the edge. She has no visible mouth. Glue the top part that touches the top of the bag only to avoid gluing the mouth shut. Glue on the dress, which is a piece of black paper cut the size of the bottom of the bag on the paper cutter. Glue on the chin. Glue hatband on hat and glue hat on. Glue on arms by folding about 1/2 edge of sleeve to the back and gluing it down. Glue hands to the back of the sleeve so that the lines are visible. The arms have a hinged effect. Glue the legs to the back of the skirt.

PARENT MEMO

Today's date: _____

Child's name: _____

Dear Parent:

Please set aside five minutes a day to work on these exercises for initial /gr/.

Please read these words to your child every day. Your child is to listen, but not repeat them to you.

grain	gray	grim	groove	growl
grand	green	grind	grouch	grunt
grape	grew	groom	group	grumble

Your child should practice saying these each day. Check off each time he or she says the words to you.

grade
0 0 0 0 0

grapes
0 0 0 0 0

graph
0 0 0 0 0

grass
0 0 0 0 0

gravy
0 0 0 0 0

grill
0 0 0 0 0

Helping your child with speech homework will be an important advantage for your child's progress. If your child experiences difficulty or frustration, stop. Try to make your sessions brief and positive. If you want to further enrich your child's speech program and language development, you might consider checking out any of the following books from the library and reading them with your child. They contain initial /gr/ in the titles.

Amazing Grace by Mary Hoffman
The Grouchy Ladybug by Eric Carle
Greedy Zebra edited by Mwenye Hadithi
I Was a Second Grade Werewolf by Daniel M. Pinkwater

Songs you can sing emphasizing initial /gr/ are "Green Grass Grew All Around" and "Ground Hog."

Thank you for your support. Please sign and return this when you have completed the above lessons.

Additional Teacher Comment *(optional):*

Parent signature _____

Please write your comments, if any, on the back of this memo.

GRUMPY GRAM ACTIVITY PAGE

Color the pictures that begin with /gr/.

GRUMPY GRAM PUPPET PATTERNS

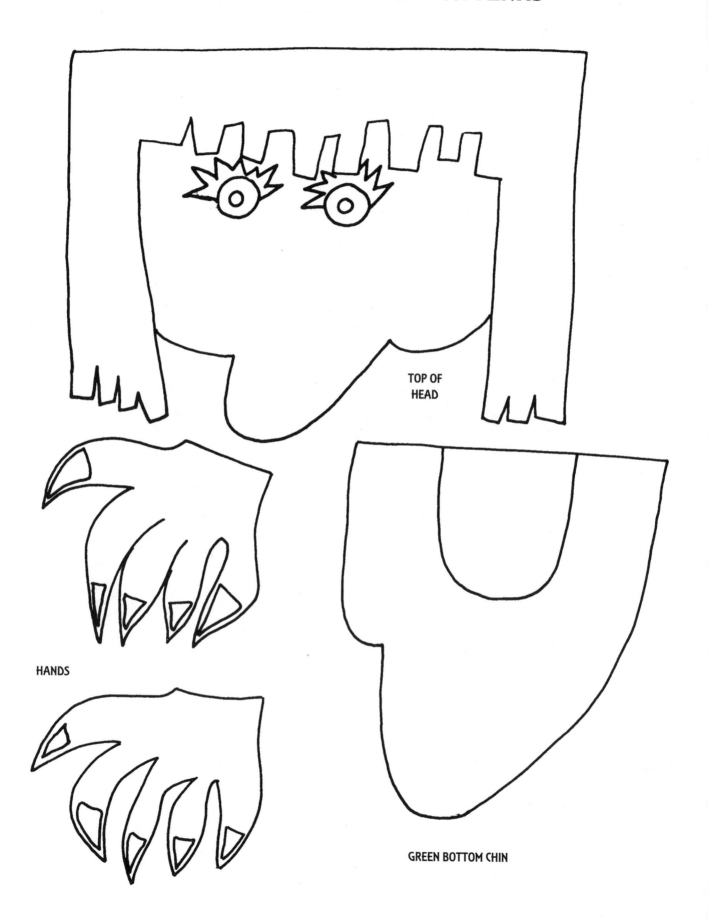

TOP OF
HEAD

HANDS

GREEN BOTTOM CHIN

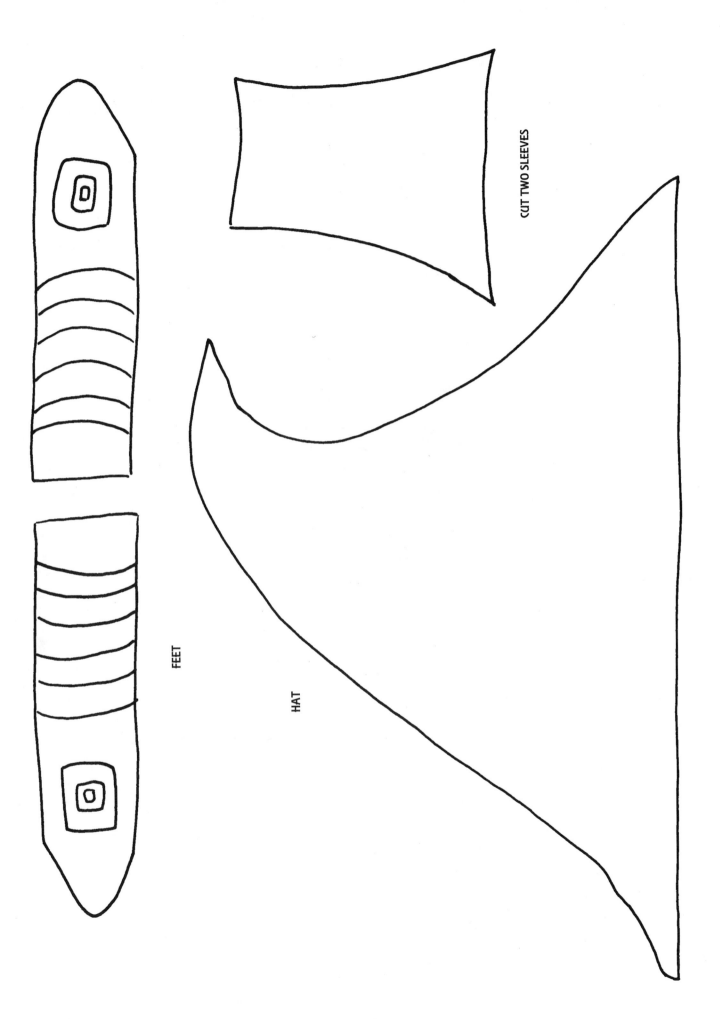

FEET

HAT

CUT TWO SLEEVES

GRUMPY GRAM B&W FLANNEL BOARD FIGURE

62

GRUMPY GRAM B&W FLANNEL BOARD FIGURES

64

63

PLAID PLATYPUS

FLANNEL BOARD STORY

The platypus is one of the oddest looking animals you will see any place on the planet. It has fur, not plumes, but has a bill and feet like a duck. It plunges in the water with a plop and plucks plenty of worms, insects, and other small water animals, but not plants.

This is a platypus that wanted people to look at him with pleasure. He pledged to find a way to please people. Finally, this platypus came up with a plan. He put on a plaid tie. *(figure 65)* Then he didn't look so plain. Plenty of people thought the plaid tie was a real plus. They named this platypus Plaid. If you see this platypus, please be pleasant!

PLAID PLATYPUS SONG

(Can be sung to "Happy Birthday to You")

Plaid Platypus was pleased.
Plaid Platypus was pleased.
With his plaid tie he looked pleasant.
Plaid Platypus was pleased.

VOCABULARY

Initial /pl/

ONE-SYLLABLE WORDS

place	plank	plead	plop	plug
plaid	plant	please	plot	plum
plain	plaque	pleat	plow	plume
plan	plate	pledge	pluck	plus
plane	play	plod		

TWO-SYLLABLE WORDS

placid	plaster	player	plaza	pliers
planet	plastic	playful	pleasant	plumber
plankton	platform	playground	pleasure	plunger
plasma	platoon	playpen	plenty	plural

PLAID PLATYPUS PUPPET

Materials:

brown and black construction paper;

black crayon;

white gummed reinforcers for eyes;

plaid wrapping paper or plaid wallpaper *(optional)*;

lunch bag;

scissors;

glue

Directions:

1. Duplicate the patterns on construction paper. Cut off one inch from the bottom of the bag.

2. Outline with black. Color inside of mouth with black. Color feet black.

3. Cut out all pieces. Glue on head. Glue on bill. It hangs over quite a way, so be careful not to glue it to the bottom portion of the bag. Glue on body. Put on white reinforcers for eyes and fill in center with black crayon. Trace tie onto plaid wallpaper or wrapping paper if desired, or make up your own plaid pattern, or leave off.

PARENT MEMO

Today's date: _____

Child's name: _____

Dear Parent:

Please set aside five minutes a day to work on these exercises for initial /pl/.

Please read these words to your child every day. Your child is to listen, but not repeat them to you.

place	planet	plead	plod	pluck
plain	plank	please	plop	plum
plan	play	pledge	plot	plus

Your child should practice saying these each day. Check off each time he or she says the words to you.

plaid
O O O O O

plane
O O O O O

plant
O O O O O

plate
O O O O O

plug
O O O O O

plum
O O O O O

Helping your child with speech homework will be an important advantage for your child's progress. If your child experiences difficulty or frustration, stop. Try to make your sessions brief and positive.

Thank you for your support. Please sign and return this when you have completed the above lessons.

Additional Teacher Comment *(optional):*

Parent signature _____

Please write your comments, if any, on the back of this memo.

PLAID PLATYPUS ACTIVITY PAGE

Color the pictures that begin with /pl/.

PLAID PLATYPUS PUPPET PATTERNS

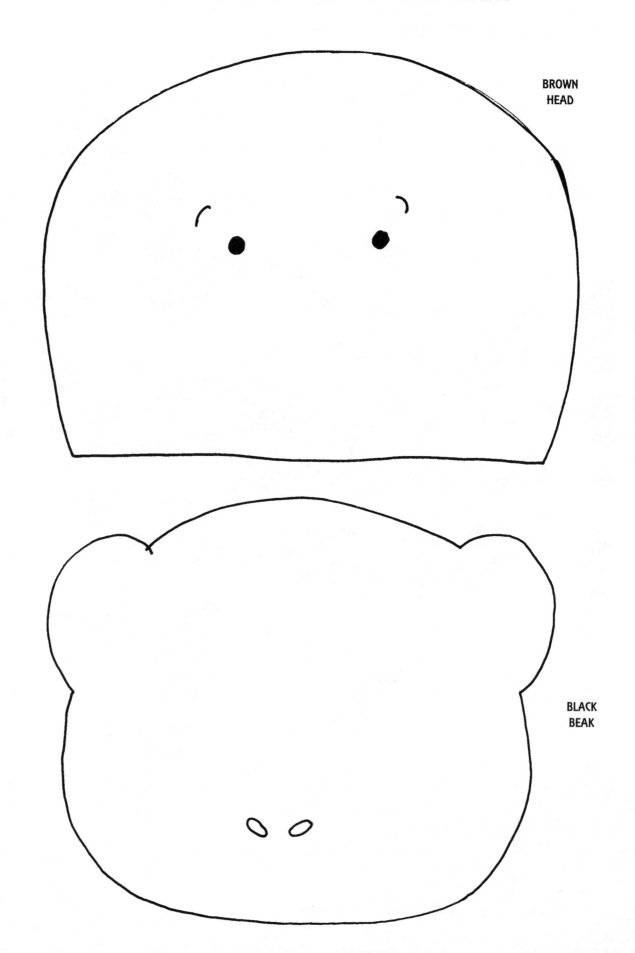

BROWN
HEAD

BLACK
BEAK

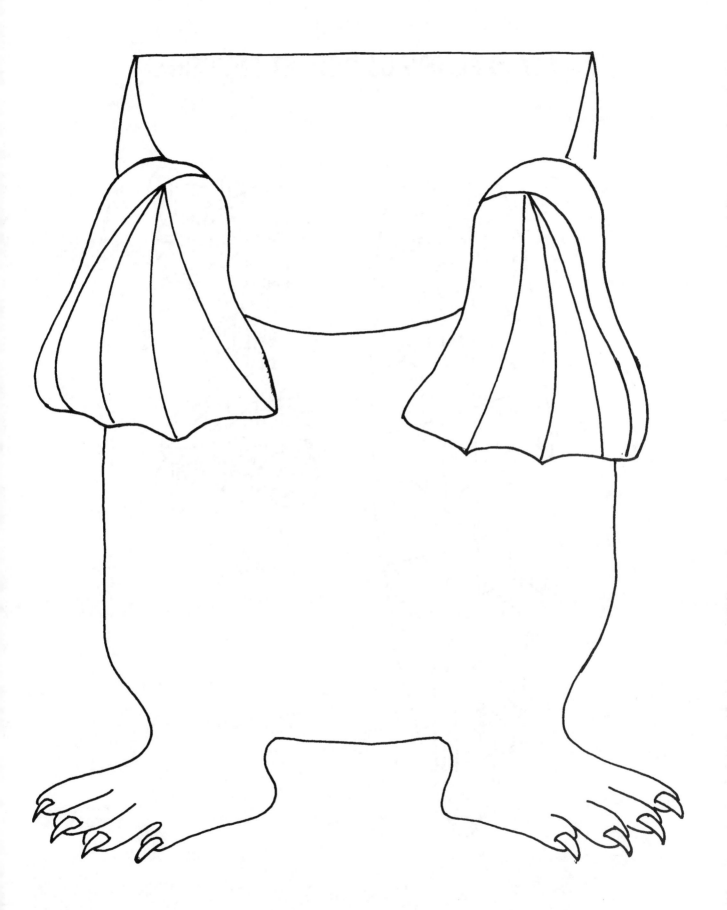

PLAID PLATYPUS PUPPET PATTERNS

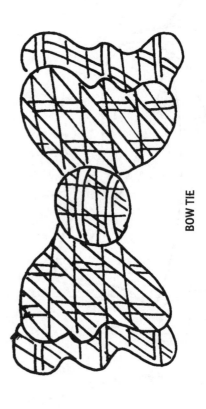

BOW TIE

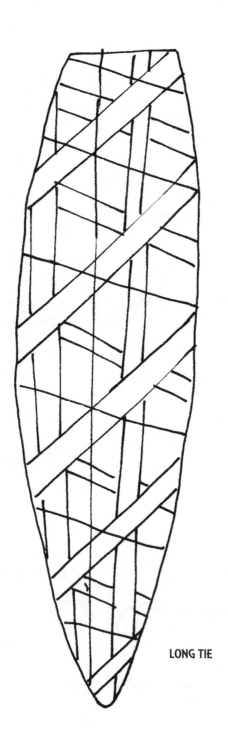

LONG TIE

PLAID PLATYPUS B&W FLANNEL BOARD FIGURE

65

PRISONER PRINCE

FLANNEL BOARD STORY

There was once a proud prince who lived on private property. He was preparing to proclaim his promise to wed a prim, proper, and pretty princess.

Before he could propose, a wicked witch caused a problem. She promptly said, "Presto!" and the prince became a frog. *(figure 66)* What a prank the predatory witch pulled on the privileged prince! The prim and proper princess will have to prepare to kiss a frog before she can presume to see the preacher with the prince. *(figure 67)* What a predicament!

PRISONER PRINCE SONG

(Can be sung to "A Bicycle Built for Two")

Princess, Princess, prepare to kiss a frog.
Pray, be thankful it isn't a snake or hog.
He's the proudest prince you've seen
The problem is he's green.
Prepare to kiss, you prim princess,
And he'll promptly pronounce you queen!

VOCABULARY

Initial /pr/

ONE-SYLLABLE WORDS

praise	price	probe	proud
prance	pride	prod	prove
prank	prime	prom	prowl
prawn	primp	prompt	prude
pray	prince	prone	prune
preach	print	proof	pry
preen	prize	prop	
press	pro	prose	

TWO-SYLLABLE WORDS

practice	prefer	pressure	pretzel	problem
prairie	prepare	presto	princess	proclaim
preacher	preschool	pretend	prison	program
precious	present	pretty	private	promise

PRISONER PRINCE PUPPET

Materials:

green construction paper;

yellow, black, green, and white crayons or oil pastels;

orange yarn *(optional);*

lunch bag;

scissors;

glue

Directions:

1. Duplicate the patterns on construction paper. Cut off three inches from the bottom of the bag.

2. Outline with black. Color inside of mouth black. Heavily color eyes yellow. Color pupil black and a white highlight at the top. Color the eyelids on the side dark green.

3. Cut out and glue to bag. For a fun touch, glue in a piece of orange yarn for the frog's tongue.

PARENT MEMO

Today's date: _____

Child's name: _____

Dear Parent:

Please set aside five minutes a day to work on these exercises for initial /pr/.

Please read these words to your child every day. Your child is to listen, but not repeat them to you.

praise	precious	price	pro	prove
prance	press	pride	prompt	prowl
pray	presto	print	proud	pry

Your child should practice saying these each day. Check off each time he or she says the words to you.

prawn
0 0 0 0 0

price
0 0 0 0 0

prince
0 0 0 0 0

print
0 0 0 0 0

prize
0 0 0 0 0

prune
0 0 0 0 0

Helping your child with speech homework will be an important advantage for your child's progress. If your child experiences difficulty or frustration, stop. Try to make your sessions brief and positive. If you want to further enrich your child's speech program and language development, you might consider checking out any of the following books from the library and reading them with your child. They contain initial /pr/ in the titles.

Frog Prince (any version)
The Princess and the Pea by Hans Christian Andersen

Thank you for your support. Please sign and return this when you have completed the above lessons.

Additional Teacher Comment *(optional):*

Parent signature _____

Please write your comments, if any, on the back of this memo.

PRISONER PRINCE ACTIVITY PAGE

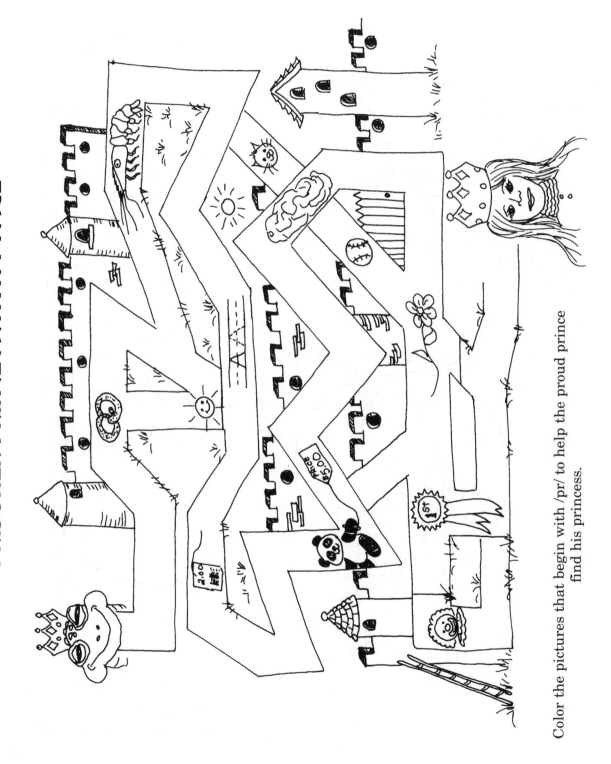

Color the pictures that begin with /pr/ to help the proud prince find his princess.

PRISONER PRINCE PUPPET PATTERN

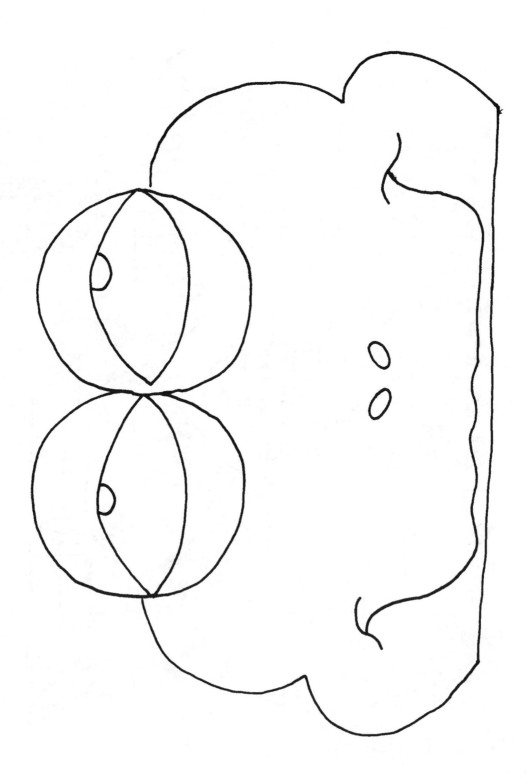

PRISONER PRINCE PUPPET PATTERN

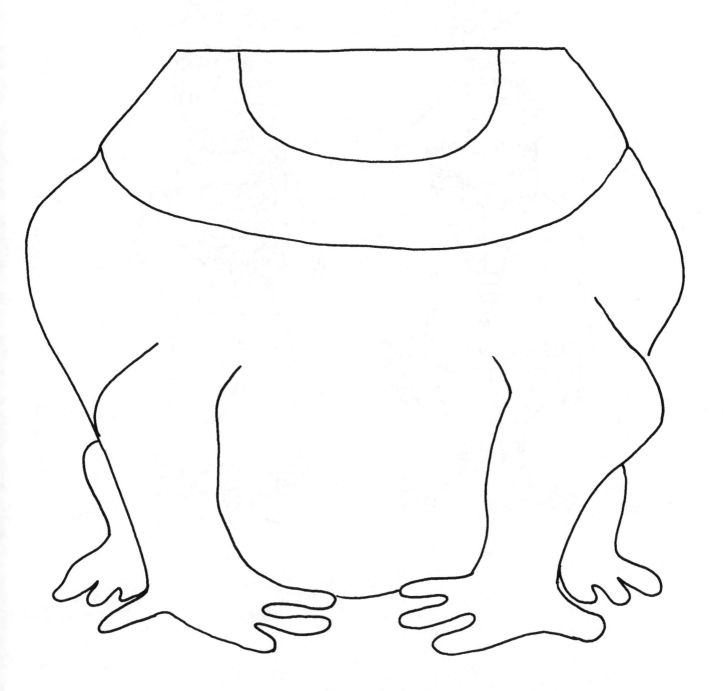

PRISONER PRINCE B&W FLANNEL BOARD FIGURES

66

67

244

SHERMAN SHARK

FLANNEL BOARD STORY

Shh! Sherman Shark might be shimmering in the shallow shadows! *(figure 68)* Sherman is shrewd as he looks for things to shatter with his sharp teeth. He will eat shrimp *(figure 69,)* shellfish *(figure 70,)* shoes *(figure 71,)* or a sheriff! *(figure 72)*

If you see Sherman near shore, give a shout or a shrill shriek. He's enough to make you shudder and shiver!

SHERMAN POEM

(Can be sung to "There Is a Tavern in the Town")

Shhh! Look out for Sherman Shark,
He doesn't shriek, he doesn't bark.
He shrewdly lurks in shallow shores
With sharp shark teeth he explores.

VOCABULARY

Initial /sh/

ONE-SYLLABLE WORDS

shack	shark	shelf	shirt	shot
shade	sharp	shell	shock	show
shaft	shave	shhh!	shoe	shrewd
shake	shed	shield	shy	shriek
sham	she	shift	shoot	shrimp
shame	sheep	shin	shop	shrivel
shape	sheer	shine	shore	shut
share	sheet	ship	short	shy

TWO-SYLLABLE WORDS

shabby	shatter	Sherman	shortcake	shudder
shadow	shellac	shimmer	shortening	shuffle
shaggy	shellfish	shingle	shoulder	shutter
shallow	sherbet	shiver	shovel	shuttle
shampoo	sheriff			

SHERMAN SHARK PUPPET

Materials:

white construction paper;

red, white, and yellow crayons;

very watery black tempera or gray watercolor for wash;

lunch bag;

scissors;

glue

Directions:

1. Duplicate the patterns on construction paper. Cut off three inches from the bottom of the bag.

2. *This is a crayon resist, so all coloring must be done firmly.* Color in eyes with yellow. Color teeth white. Color inside of mouth red. Color checkered napkin red. You don't need to color the white squares. Outline gills, eyes, and center of eyes with black. With very watery paint, wash shark's body. Let dry.

3. Cut out all pieces. Glue on top of head. Nose hangs down a bit. Glue on bottom of figure and fins. Glue on napkin.

PARENT MEMO

Today's date: _____

Child's name: _____

Dear Parent:

Please set aside five minutes a day to work on these exercises for initial /sh/.

Please read these words to your child every day. Your child is to listen, but not repeat them to you.

shampoo	sharp	sheet	shellfish	shoe
shape	she	shelf	sheriff	short
shark	sheep	shell	shirt	shut

Your child should practice saying these each day. Check off each time he or she says the words to you.

shapes
0 0 0 0 0

shark
0 0 0 0 0

sheep
0 0 0 0 0

shell
0 0 0 0 0

ship
0 0 0 0 0

shoe
0 0 0 0 0

Helping your child with speech homework will be an important advantage for your child's progress. If your child experiences difficulty or frustration, stop. Try to make your sessions brief and positive. If you want to further enrich your child's speech program and language development, you might consider checking out any of the following books from the library and reading them with your child. They contain initial /sh/ in the titles.

Nothing Sticks Like a Shadow by Ann Tompert
Sheep in a Jeep by Nancy Shar
She'll be Comin' Round the Mountain by Robert Quackenbush
Shh! by Suzy Kline
The Shoemaker and the Elves by The Brothers Grimm

Songs you can sing emphasizing initial /sh/ are "She'll Be Comin' Round the Mountain," "You Are My Sunshine," and "Shake My Sillies Out."

Thank you for your support. Please sign and return this when you have completed the above lessons.

Additional Teacher Comment *(optional):*

Parent signature _____

Please write your comments, if any, on the back of this memo.

SHERMAN SHARK ACTIVITY PAGE

Color the pictures that begin with /sh/.

©1996 by Elizabeth Krepelin and Bonnie Mae Smith

248

SHERMAN SHARK PUPPET PUZZLE

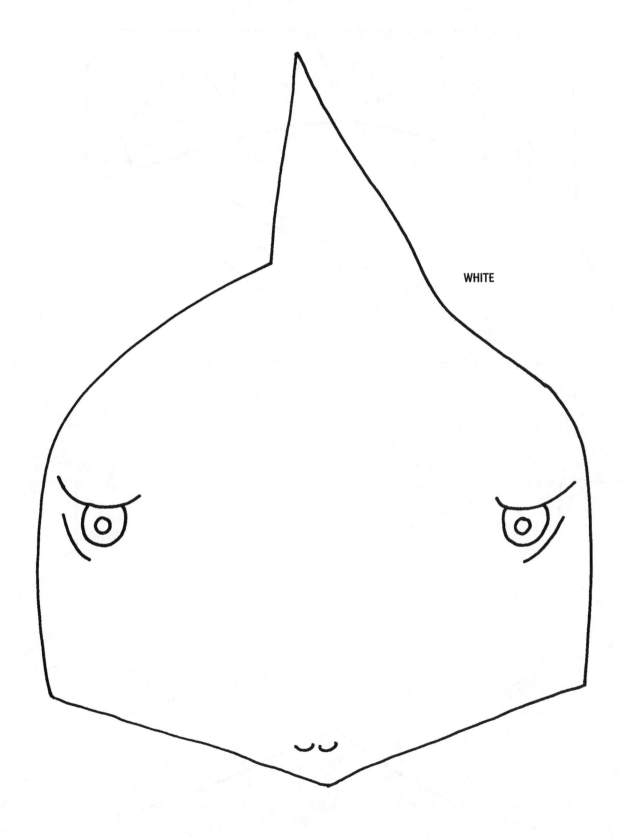

WHITE

SHERMAN SHARK PUPPET PATTERN

WHITE
BODY

SHERMAN SHARK PUPPET PATTERN

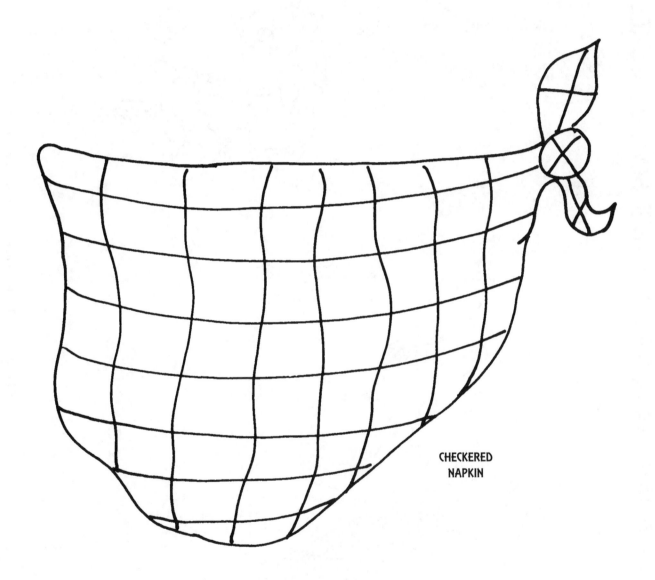

CHECKERED
NAPKIN

SHERMAN SHARK B&W FLANNEL BOARD FIGURES

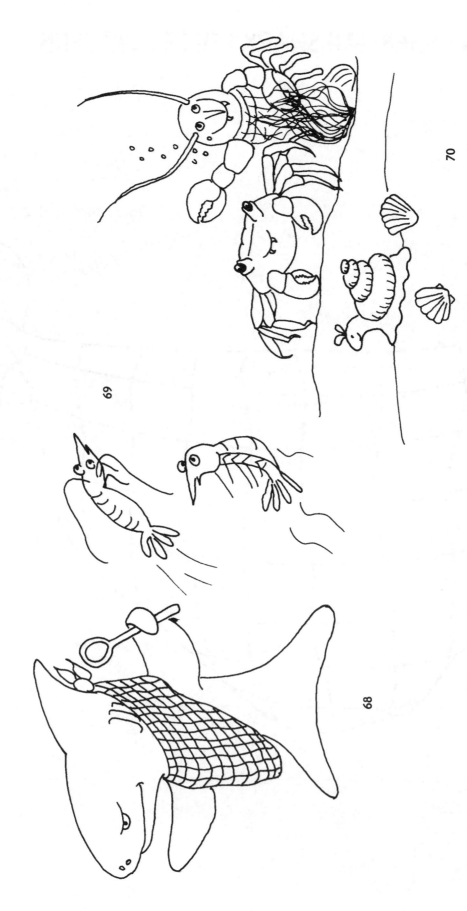

69

70

68

SHERMAN SHARK B&W FLANNEL BOARD FIGURES

71

72

SKIP SCARECROW

FLANNEL BOARD STORY

Skip Scarecrow *(figure 73)* wears a scarlet hat. He lives in a cornfield in Scarsdale. He is a scout who scans the sky for scoundrel crows. They scavenge for food and ruin Farmer Scott's crop. What a scandal!

Skip is part of Farmer Scott's scheme to scatter the crows and get his corn to market on schedule. *(figure 74)* When those scamps, the crows, see Skip, they scream, screech, scramble, and scuttle away to another field. Skip is no fool; he was the number one scholar at scarecrow school. Farmer Scott doesn't scold because Skip makes the scoundrels scat!

SKIP SCARECROW SONG

(Can be sung to "Skinamarink" chorus)

Scat crows, scamper, scoot,
Scramble, skitter, shoo!
Go away, please do!
Scat crows, scamper, scoot,
Scramble, skitter, shoo!
Go away, please do!

I'll scare you in the morning
And in the heat of noon.
I'll scatter you this evening
In dark or light of moon.
Oh
(repeat chorus)

VOCABULARY

Initial /sk/

ONE-SYLLABLE WORDS

scab	scare	scope	skate	skip
scald	scarf	scorch	sketch	skirt
scale	scat	score	ski	skit
scamp	scheme	scorn	skid	skull
scan	school	scour	skill	skunk
scant	scold	scout	skim	sky
scar	scoop	scowl	skimp	
scarce	scoot	scum	skin	

TWO-SYLLABLE WORDS

scaffold	scanty	scholar	sculpture	skier
scallop	scarlet	scooter	scurry	skillet
scalpel	scary	scoreboard	skateboard	skinny
scamper	scatter	scoundrel	skeptic	skyline
scandal	schedule	scuba		

SKIP SCARECROW PUPPET

Materials:

white construction paper;

bright crayons or markers (preferred);

straw for trim, if possible;

three 2 × 12-inch strips brown construction paper;

lunch bag;

scissors;

glue

Directions:

1. Duplicate the patterns on construction paper.

2. Color scarecrow as desired. Hat should be red.

3. Outline with black, except for bottom straight line on scarecrow head.

4. Cut out pieces. Glue on head. Glue on chin/shirt, lining up X's of mouth. Quickly slip pants under shirt and glue to bag. Glue two strips to bag the long way, end to end, and then cross with the third strip to form a T (horizontal part looks like it comes through the sleeves) that would hang Skip in the field. Glue on real straw, if desired.

PARENT MEMO

Today's date: _____

Child's name: _____

Dear Parent:

Please set aside five minutes a day to work on these exercises for initial /sk/.

Please read these words to your child every day. Your child is to listen, but not repeat them to you.

scamp	scare	scold	scout	sketch
scan	scary	scoot	scum	skim
scar	scheme	score	scurry	skin

Your child should practice saying these each day. Check off each time he or she says the words to you.

scale
O O O O O

school
O O O O O

skate
O O O O O

ski
O O O O O

skirt
O O O O O

skull
O O O O O

Helping your child with speech homework will be an important advantage for your child's progress. If your child experiences difficulty or frustration, stop. Try to make your sessions brief and positive. If you want to further enrich your child's speech program and language development, you might consider checking out any of the following books from the library and reading them with your child. They contain initial /sk/ in the titles.

Morris Goes to School by Bernard Wiseman
Scary, Scary Halloween by Eve Bunting
We Laughed a Lot, My First Day of School by Sylvia R. Tester

Songs you can sing emphasizing initial /sk/ are "School Days," "Scat Like That," "Skip to My Lou," and "Skinamarink."

Thank you for your support. Please sign and return this when you have completed the above lessons.

Additional Teacher Comment *(optional):*

Parent signature _____

Please write your comments, if any, on the back of this memo.

SKIP SCARECROW ACTIVITY PAGE

Use your eyes carefully! Color all the pictures that begin with /sk/.

SKIP SCARECROW PUPPET PATTERN

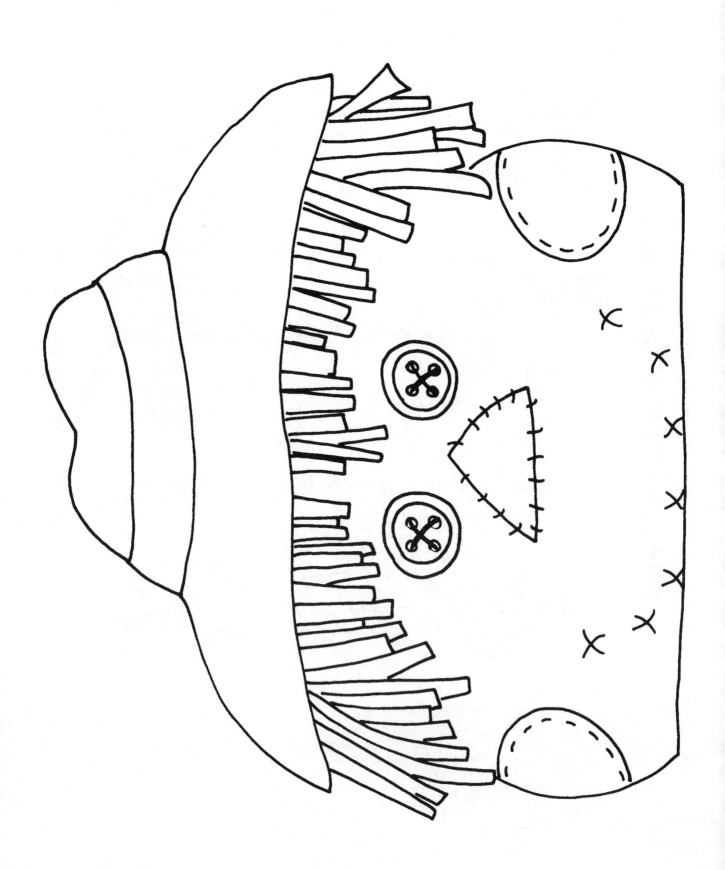

SKIP SCARECROW PUPPET PATTERN

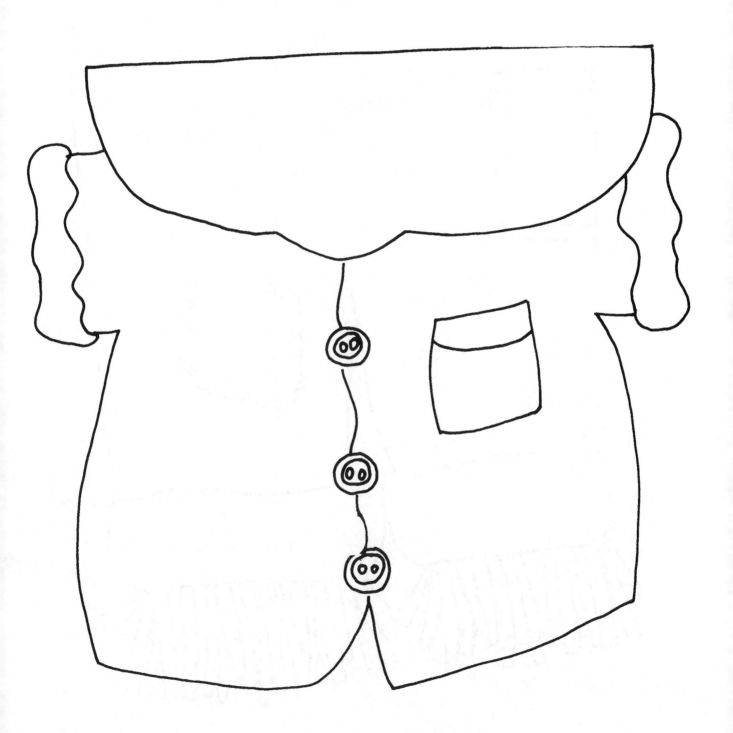

SKIP SCARECROW PUPPET PATTERN

SKIP SCARECROW B&W FLANNEL BOARD FIGURE

73

SKIP SCARECROW B&W FLANNEL BOARD FIGURE

74

SLOW SLOANE

FLANNEL BOARD STORY

Sloane is slow, but all turtles are *(figure 75)*. He doesn't see the slightest reason to hurry. If he is on a slope or the ground is slippery, he sometimes likes to slide or slosh along or use his tummy as a sled. *(figure 76)*

He is no slob or slouch. He doesn't sleep very much. He gets things done in his own good time. He is slight, slim and sleek, but he is also very, very slow.

SLOW SLOANE SONG

(Can be sung to "Frosty the Snowman")

Slow Sloane the turtle
Doesn't slide or slip along.
You could call him slow
And be in the know.
Call him quick and you'd be wrong.

Slim, slight and sleek
He likes to take his time.
But he's quick to say
As he's on his way
Going slowly is no crime.

VOCABULARY

Initial /sl/

ONE-SYLLABLE WORDS

slab	slave	slept	slip	slow
slack	slaw	slew	slit	sludge
slam	sled	slick	sloop	slug
slang	sleek	slide	slope	slump
slant	sleep	slight	slot	slurp
slap	sleeve	slim	sloth	slush
slash	sleigh	sling	slouch	sly
slate				

Two-syllable words

sledder	slender	slipper	slogan	slowdown
sleepless	slicker	slither	sloppy	sluggish
sleepy	slimy	sliver	slouchy	slumber
sleeveless	slingshot	slobber		

SLOW SLOANE PUPPET

Materials:

green construction paper;

black and a variety of other colors of crayons;

lunch bag;

scissors;

glue

Directions:

1. Duplicate the patterns on construction paper. Cut off five inches from the bottom of the bag.

2. Outline with black. Choose two colors for the shell and any color you want for glasses. The turtle's body is the green color of the construction paper. The half circle above the head is orange, or any color you choose. Color hard. The swirled design of the shell could be brown, or any other color. The outer edge of the shell can be orange, or your choice. Color stripes on its stomach and nails as you wish. Color glasses.

3. Cut out. Glue head to bag; nose hangs down a bit. Glue body to bag, matching up top and bottom lines carefully.

PARENT MEMO

Today's date: _____

Child's name: _____

Dear Parent:

Please set aside five minutes a day to work on these exercises for initial /sl/.

Please read these words to your child every day. Your child is to listen, but not repeat them to you.

slab	slap	slick	slope	slump
slam	slash	slight	slouch	slurp
slang	sleek	sling	slow	sly

Your child should practice saying these each day. Check off each time he or she says the words to you.

sled
0 0 0 0 0

sleep
0 0 0 0 0

sleeve
0 0 0 0 0

sleigh
0 0 0 0 0

slide
0 0 0 0 0

slip
0 0 0 0 0

Helping your child with speech homework will be an important advantage for your child's progress. If your child experiences difficulty or frustration, stop. Try to make your sessions brief and positive. If you want to further enrich your child's speech program and language development, check out the book *Going to Sleep on the Farm* by Wendy C. Lewison. Sing "Are You Sleeping?" Both of these titles feature initial /sl/.

Thank you for your support. Please sign and return this when you have completed the above lessons.

Additional Teacher Comment *(optional)*:

Parent signature _____

Please write your comments, if any, on the back of this memo.

SLOW SLOANE ACTIVITY PAGE

Circle the pictures that begin with /sl/.

SLOW SLOANE PUPPET PATTERN

SLOW SLOANE PUPPET PATTERN

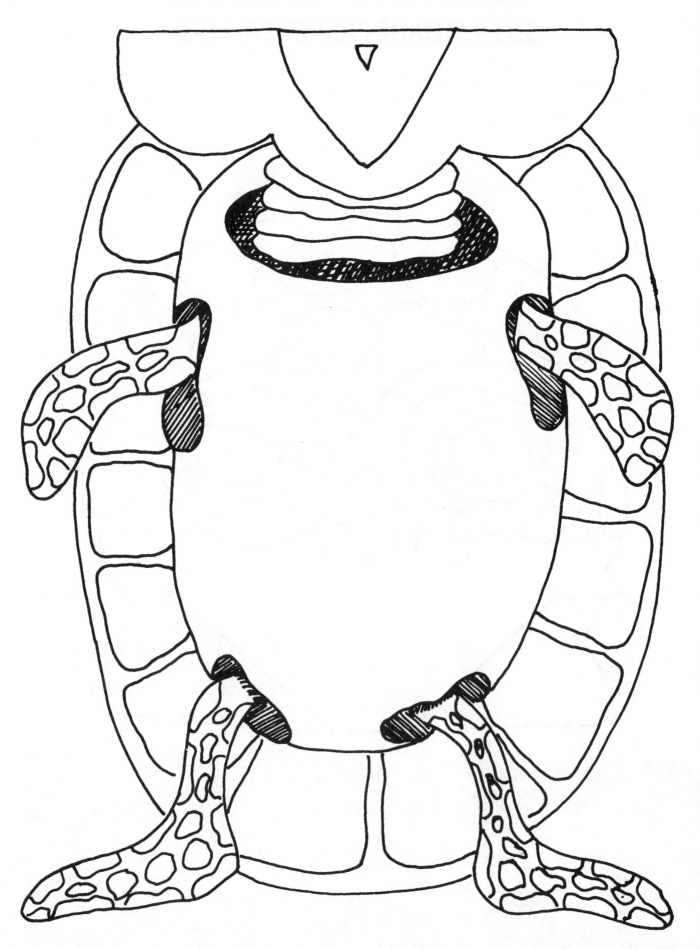

SLOW SLOANE B&W FLANNEL BOARD FIGURES

75

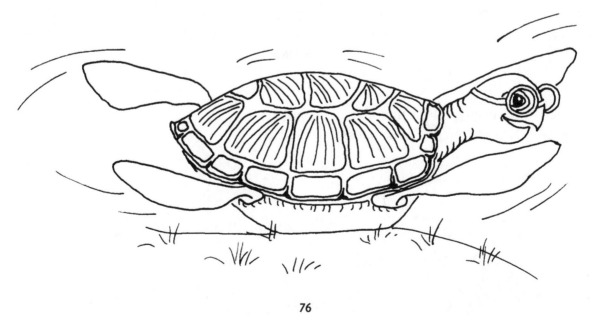

76

SMELL SMALL

FLANNEL BOARD STORY

(figure 77) Smell Small is a smart skunk with a smoldering smell. No one smirks or smacks at Smell. She's smug and wears a smile because no one wants to be smeared with that smell. Remember, when you see Smell, smile!

SMELL SMALL SONG

(Can be sung to "B-I-N-G-O")

Follow the same pattern of clapping as you say the letters of the name, repeating five times until you clap the whole name.

There was a skunk who truly stunk
And Smell was her name:
S-M-E-L-L, S-M-E-L-L, S-M-E-L-L
And Smell was her name!

VOCABULARY

Initial /sm/

ONE-SYLLABLE WORDS

smack	smear	smirch	smock	smooch
smart	smell	smirk	smog	smooth
smash	smile	smite	smoke	smug

TWO-SYLLABLE WORDS

smaller	smelly	smocking	smolder
smarter	smidgen	smokeless	smother

SMELL SMALL PUPPET

Materials:

black, white, and pink construction paper;

carbon paper *(optional);*

white hole reinforcers;

bright paper or wallpaper for coveralls;

lunch bag;

scissors;

glue

Directions:

1. Duplicate the patterns on construction paper.

2. Using a pattern trace black parts onto black construction paper, or use carbon paper. If you are using wallpaper for the coveralls, trace the coveralls onto the wallpaper.

3. Cut out all parts. Glue on head. Glue on body. Glue on coveralls. Glue on pink nose and white fluffy hair on top. Glue tail to back of bag. Glue on reinforcers for eyes.

PARENT MEMO

Today's date: _____

Child's name: _____

Dear Parent:

Please set aside five minutes a day to work on these exercises for initial /sm/.

Please read these words to your child every day. Your child is to listen, but not repeat them to you.

smack	smash	smidgen	smock	smooch
smaller	smear	smirch	smog	smooth
smart	smelly	smirk	smolder	smug

Your child should practice saying these each day. Check off each time he or she says the words to you.

small
O O O O O

smash
O O O O O

smile
O O O O O

smock
O O O O O

smoke
O O O O O

smooth
O O O O O

Helping your child with speech homework will be an important advantage for your child's progress. If your child experiences difficulty or frustration, stop. Try to make your sessions brief and positive. If you want to further enrich your child's speech program and language development, sing "When You're Smiling," "Smoky the Bear," and "It's A Small World." These songs have words that begin with /sm/ in their titles and lyrics.

Thank you for your support. Please sign and return this when you have completed the above lessons.

Additional Teacher Comment *(optional)*:

Parent signature _____

Please write your comments, if any, on the back of this memo.

SMELL SMALL ACTIVITY PAGE

Color the pictures that begin with /sm/.

SMELL SMALL PUPPET PATTERNS

BLACK

PINK
NOSE

WHITE
HAIR

SMELL SMALL PUPPET PATTERN

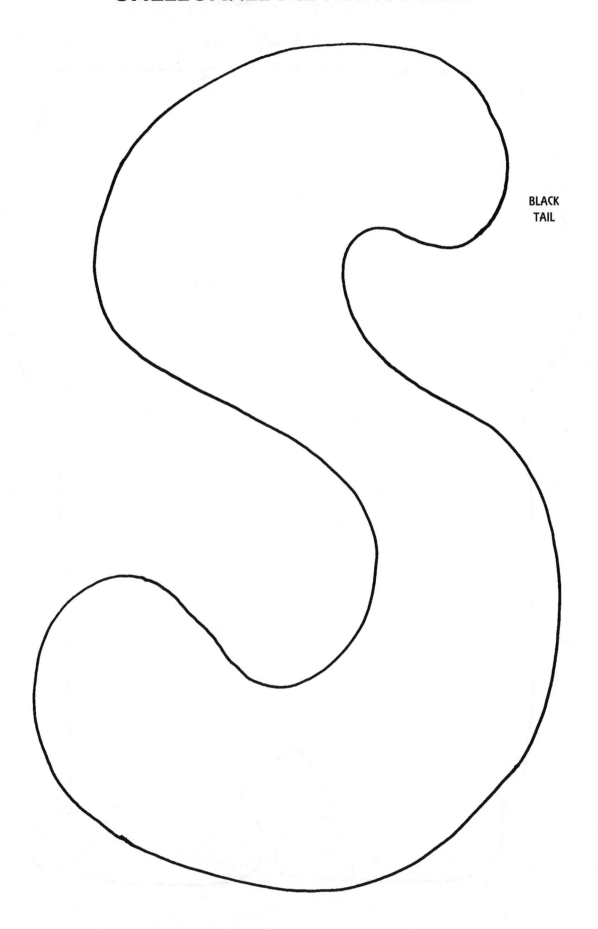

BLACK
TAIL

SMELL SMALL PUPPET PATTERN

BLACK

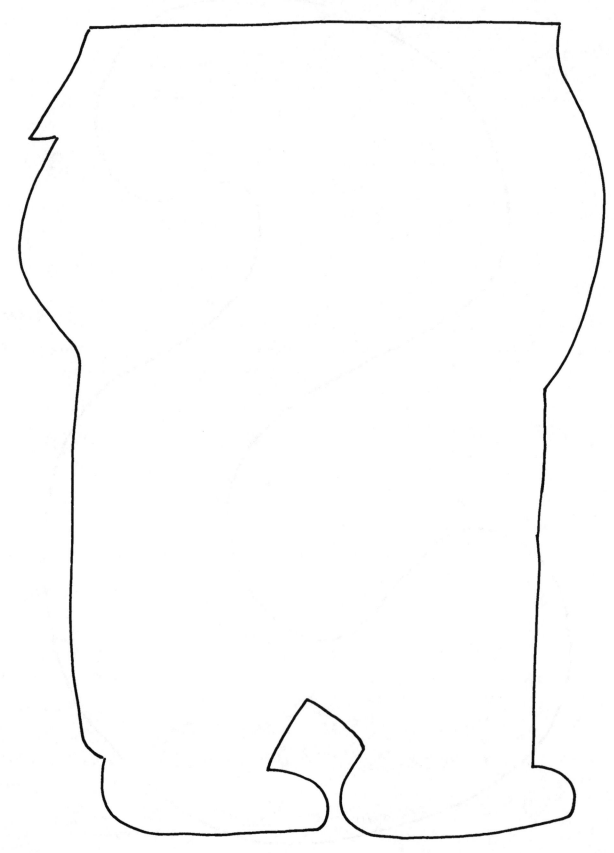

SMELL SMALL PUPPET PATTERN

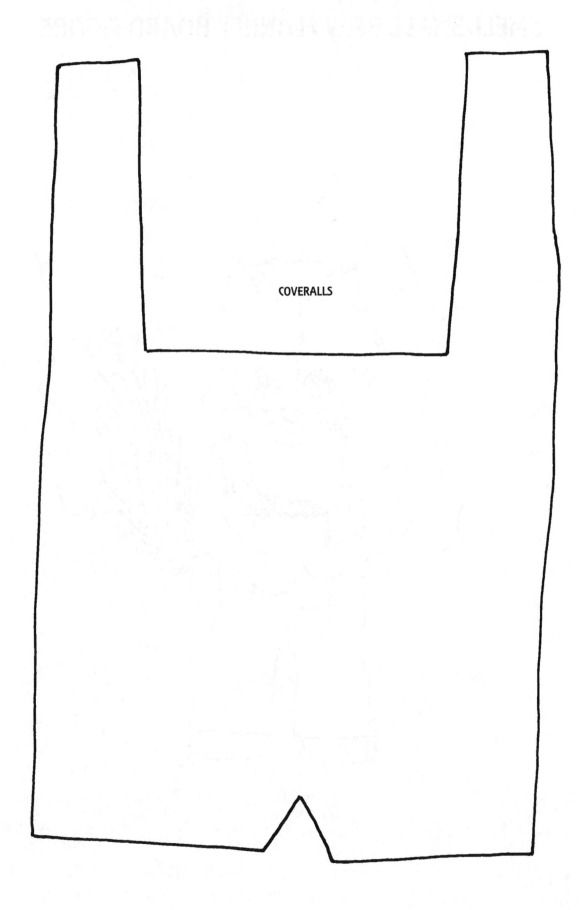

COVERALLS

SMELL SMALL B&W FLANNEL BOARD FIGURE

77

SNOW MAN

FLANNEL BOARD STORY

(figure 78) Snow Man is a snappy dresser. He wears a snazzy scarf. He is made of snowflakes. He is very cold, but he doesn't sneeze, sniff, snivel, snarl, snoop, sneak, snack, snooze, or snore. Snow Man is not a snob. He'd never snub anyone who might want to snuggle.

SNOW MAN SONG

(Can be sung to "Do Your Ears Hang Low?")

I am made of snow
From my head down to my toe.
I'm the snazziest fellow
You will ever get to know.
I don't snivel, snooze, or sneeze
In the coldest winter breeze.
I am made of snow.

VOCABULARY

Initial /sn/

ONE-SYLLABLE WORDS

snack	snare	sneeze	snoop	snout
snag	snarl	snide	snoot	snow
snail	sneak	snip	snooze	snub
snap	sneer	snob	snore	snug

TWO-SYLLABLE WORDS

snazzy	snicker	snooty	snowflake	snuggle
sneakers	sniffle	snorkel	snowman	

SNOW MAN PUPPET

Materials:

white and black construction paper;

yellow, orange, red, blue, brown, and black crayons;

lunch bag;

scissors;

glue

Directions:

1. Duplicate the patterns on construction paper.

2. Trace hat onto black paper. Outline snowman and all parts with black.

3. Cut out all parts. Glue on head. Glue on hat. Using scraps of paper or crayons, decorate scarf, and add details of face and accessories to the snowman.

PARENT MEMO

Today's date: _____

Child's name: _____

Dear Parent:

Please set aside five minutes a day to work on these exercises for initial /sn/.

Please read these words to your child every day. Your child is to listen, but not repeat them to you.

snag	snazzy	sneer	sniffle	snoot
snare	sneak	sneeze	snip	snub
snarl	sneakers	snide	snoop	snug

Your child should practice saying these each day. Check off each time he or she says the words to you.

snack
0 0 0 0 0

snail
0 0 0 0 0

snap
0 0 0 0 0

snooze
0 0 0 0 0

snore
0 0 0 0 0

snow
0 0 0 0 0

Helping your child with speech homework will be an important advantage for your child's progress. If your child experiences difficulty or frustration, stop. Try to make your sessions brief and positive. If you want to further enrich your child's speech program and language development, you might consider checking out any of the following books from the library and reading them with your child. They contain initial /sn/ in the titles.

Hide and Snake by Keith Baker
Sadie and the Snowman by Allan Morgan
The Snowman by Raymond Briggs
The Sneetches and Other Stories by Dr. Seuss
The Snail's Spell by Joanne Ryder

Songs you can sing emphasizing initial /sn/ are "Frosty the Snowman" and "Suzy Snowflake."

Thank you for your support. Please sign and return this when you have completed the above lessons.

Additional Teacher Comment *(optional):*

Parent signature _____

Please write your comments, if any, on the back of this memo.

SNOW MAN ACTIVITY PAGE

Color the pictures that begin with /sn/.

SNOW MAN PUPPET PATTERNS

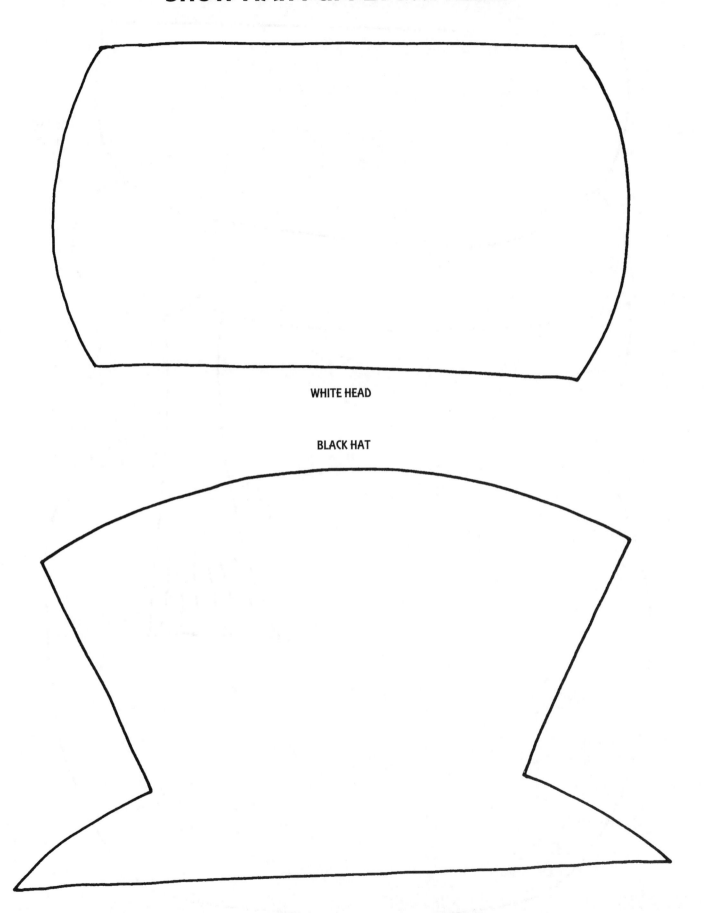

WHITE HEAD

BLACK HAT

SNOW MAN PUPPET PATTERN

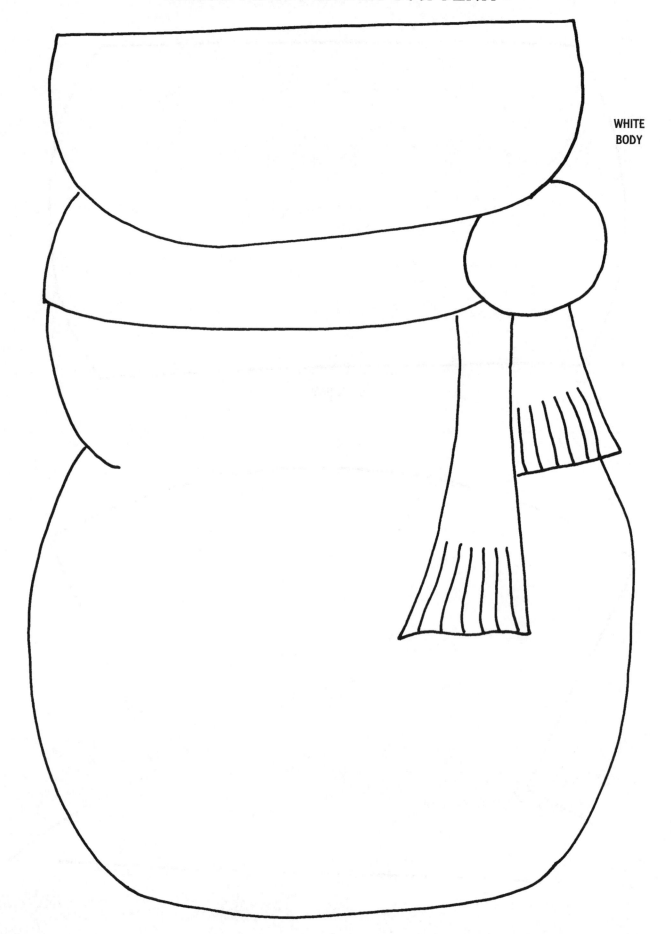

WHITE
BODY

SNOW MAN B&W FLANNEL BOARD FIGURE

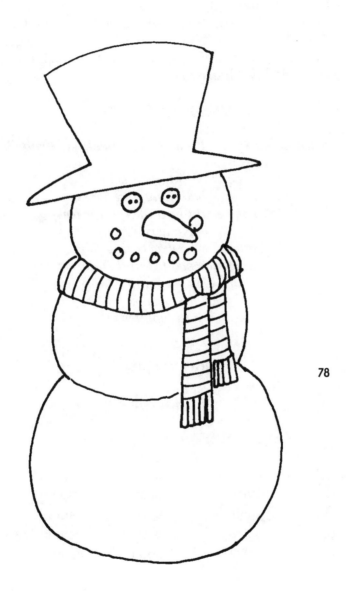

78

SPEEDY SPOT

FLANNEL BOARD STORY

Speedy Spot was a spectacular sprinter. He ate only spuds, spaghetti, and spinach, which spurred on his speed. *(figure 79)* He always spilled and made a spot on his shirt. That's how he got the name Spot.

      Spot lived by a special track in Spain where he had splendid races with anyone he could spy. One day when he was spanning a special space, he got a splinter. *(figure 80)* This took some of the spark out of Spot's speed. He pulled it out, and with a spurt of spirit he sprinted to victory. *(figure 81)*

SPEEDY SPOT SONG

(Can be sung to "Five Little Speckled Frogs")

Spot was quite a sport
In races both long and short.
No one could beat him in a race
(No way)
But when he was eating food
Spot was spoiled and rude.
That's why they named him
Speedy Spot.
(Spill, splat!)

VOCABULARY

Initial /sp/

ONE-SYLLABLE WORDS

space	speech	spit	spool	spud
spade	spell	spite	spoon	spun
span	spend	spoil	sport	spunk
spank	spice	sponge	spot	spur
spare	spill	spoof	spouse	spurt
spear	spin	spook	spout	spy
speck	spine			

TWO-SYLLABLE WORDS

spacious	sparkling	spearmint	spider
spangle	sparrow	special	spinach
spaniel	spatter	speckle	spindle
sparkler	speaker	speedy	spinster

SPEEDY SPOT PUPPET

Materials:

white construction paper;

crayons (or marking pens) of many colors;

lunch bag;

scissors;

glue

Directions:

1. Duplicate the patterns on construction paper.

2. Outline entire figure with black. Color eyes blue. Color inside of mouth and nose pink. Color clothes, socks, and shoes as desired. Get a little crazy!

3. Cut out. Glue on head. Glue on body. Glue legs to the back of the shorts.

PARENT MEMO

Today's date: _____

Child's name: _____

Dear Parent:

Please set aside five minutes a day to work on these exercises for initial /sp/.

Please read these words to your child every day. Your child is to listen, but not repeat them to you.

space	special	speedy	spin	spook
span	speck	spice	spine	sport
spare	speech	spider	spoil	spy

Your child should practice saying these each day. Check off each time he or she says the words to you.

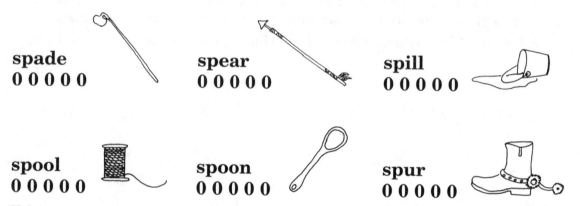

spade
0 0 0 0 0

spear
0 0 0 0 0

spill
0 0 0 0 0

spool
0 0 0 0 0

spoon
0 0 0 0 0

spur
0 0 0 0 0

Helping your child with speech homework will be an important advantage for your child's progress. If your child experiences difficulty or frustration, stop. Try to make your sessions brief and positive. If you want to further enrich your child's speech program and language development, you might consider checking out any of the following books from the library and reading them with your child. They contain initial /sp/ in the titles.

Anansi the Spider: A Tale from the Ashanti illustrated and retold by Gerald McDermott
The Eensy Weensy Spider by Joanne Oppenheim
The Snail's Spell by Joanne Ryder

Songs you can sing emphasizing initial /sp/ are "On Top of Spaghetti," "Five Little Speckled Frogs," "The Eensy Weensy Spider," and "The Star Spangled Banner."

Thank you for your support. Please sign and return this when you have completed the above lessons.

Additional Teacher Comment *(optional):*

Parent signature _____

Please write your comments, if any, on the back of this memo.

SPEEDY SPOT ACTIVITY PAGE

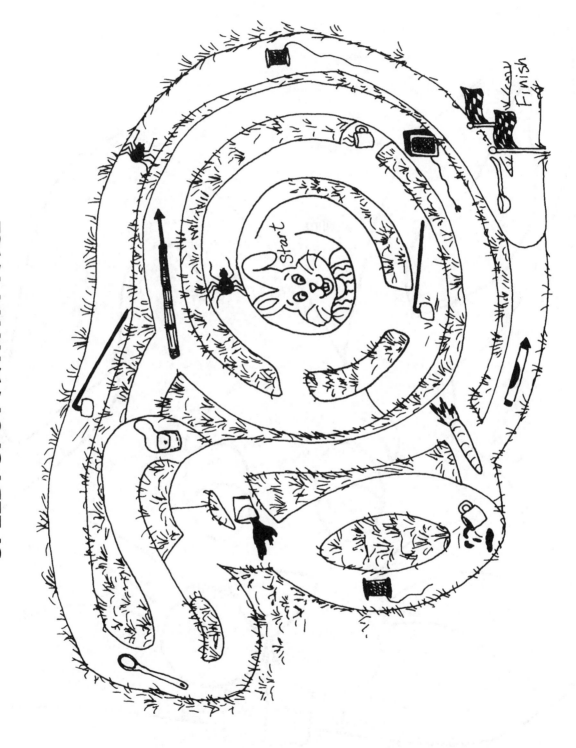

Color the pictures that begin with /sp/ to spur Spot to finish the race.

SPEEDY SPOT PUPPET PATTERN

WHITE

SPEEDY SPOT PUPPET PATTERNS

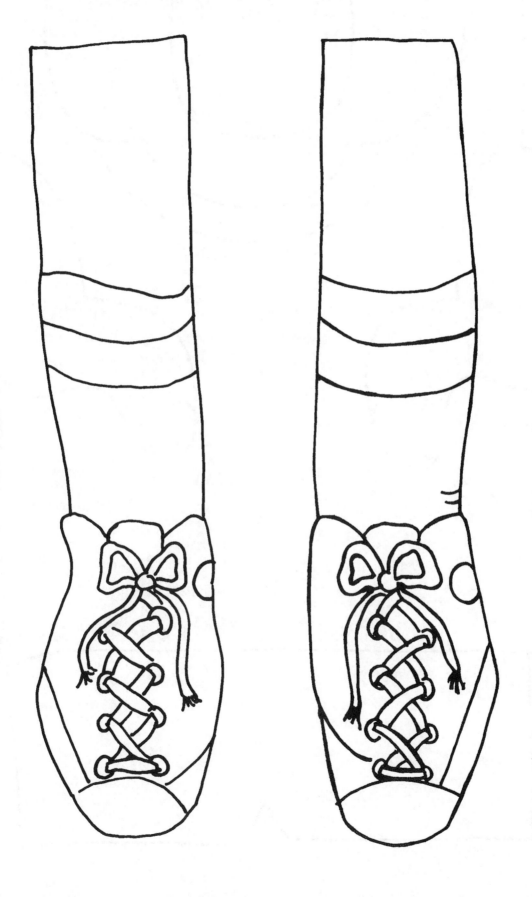

SPEEDY SPOT PUPPET PATTERN

SPEEDY SPOT B&W FLANNEL BOARD FIGURES

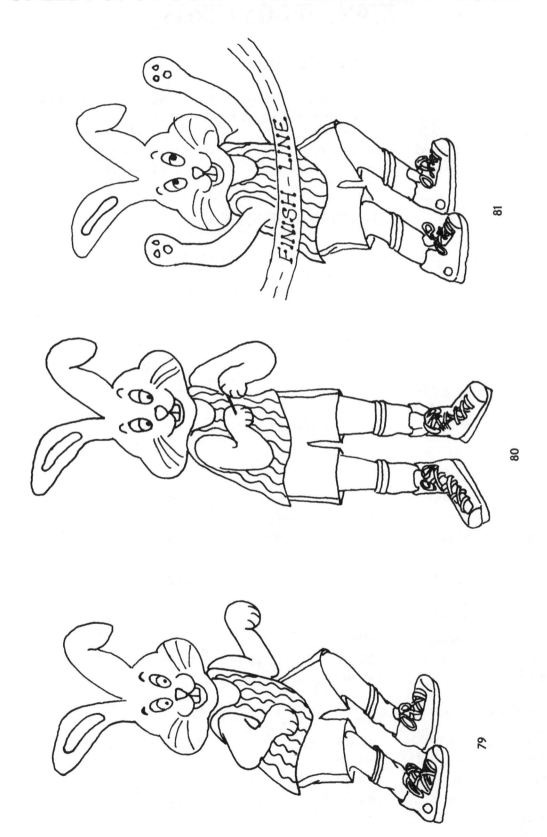

STAN STEGOSAURUS

FLANNEL BOARD STORY

(figure 82) This is a true story that started millions of years ago when the stupendous stegosaurus stomped the earth. He was a strict vegetarian, staring about for stalks and stems so he could stuff them into his stout mouth. *(figure 83)*

When he stopped finding food, he couldn't go to the store for something to eat, so he staggered and starved. The only stegosaurus you will see today is a statue.

STEGOSAURUS SIGHTING RULES

Don't stare if you see a stegosaurus.
They roamed the earth long before us.
Do not stand with mouth agape
Or try to store him on video tape.
Only stammer a courteous, "Hi."
And maybe he won't stomp you as he goes by.

VOCABULARY

Initial /st/

ONE-SYLLABLE WORDS

<u>stack</u>	<u>stand</u>	step	stole	<u>stout</u>
staff	star	stew	<u>stomp</u>	stove
<u>stage</u>	starch	stick	stone	stub
<u>stain</u>	start	stiff	stood	stud
stair	<u>state</u>	still	stool	<u>stuff</u>
stake	<u>stay</u>	stilt	stoop	stun
stale	<u>steam</u>	sting	stop	stunt
stalk	<u>steep</u>	stir	store	sty
<u>stall</u>	steer	<u>stitch</u>	<u>stork</u>	style
stamp	stem	stock	storm	

TWO-SYLLABLE WORDS

stable	stanza	<u>statue</u>	stinger	storage
stagger	staple	steady	stirrup	story
stallion	starfish	steeple	stocky	stubborn
stammer	static	sterling	stolen	student
stampede	station	sticky	stomach	stumble
standard				

STAN STEGOSAURUS PUPPET

Materials:

green or lavender construction paper;

sandpaper or tree bark *(optional)*;

dark green or black and yellow crayons;

lunch bag;

scissors;

glue

Directions:

1. Duplicate the patterns on construction paper. Cut off two inches from the bottom of the bag.

2. Outline all lines with black or dark green crayon. For a textured effect, put sandpaper or tree bark behind the paper and rub with crayon. Color inside of mouth black. Color teeth and eyes yellow.

3. Cut out. Glue on head; the nose hangs over. Glue on body.

PARENT MEMO

Today's date: _____

Child's name: _____

Dear Parent:

Please set aside five minutes a day to work on these exercises for initial /st/.

Please read these words to your child every day. Your child is to listen, but not repeat them to you.

stack	stall	statue	steep	stork
stage	stand	stay	stitch	stout
stain	state	steam	stomp	stuff

Your child should practice saying these each day. Check off each time he or she says the words to you.

stamp
0 0 0 0 0

star
0 0 0 0 0

step
0 0 0 0 0

stool
0 0 0 0 0

stop
0 0 0 0 0

stove
0 0 0 0 0

Helping your child with speech homework will be an important advantage for your child's progress. If your child experiences difficulty or frustration, stop. Try to make your sessions brief and positive. If you want to further enrich your child's speech program and language development, you might consider checking out any of the following books from the library and reading them with your child. They contain initial /st/ in the titles.

"Here's the Church, Here's the Steeple" (a finger play)
Jack and the Bean Stalk (any version)
Stone Soup by Marcia Brown
The Wolf's Chicken Stew by Keiko Kasza

Songs you can sing emphasizing initial /st/ are "Down By the Station," "Stirring the Brew," and "Twinkle, Twinkle Little Star."

Thank you for your support. Please sign and return this when you have completed the above lessons.

Additional Teacher Comment *(optional):*

Parent signature _____

Please write your comments, if any, on the back of this memo.

STAN STEGOSAURUS ACTIVITY PAGE

Color the pictures that begin with /st/. Look carefully!

STAN STEGOSAURUS PUPPET PATTERN

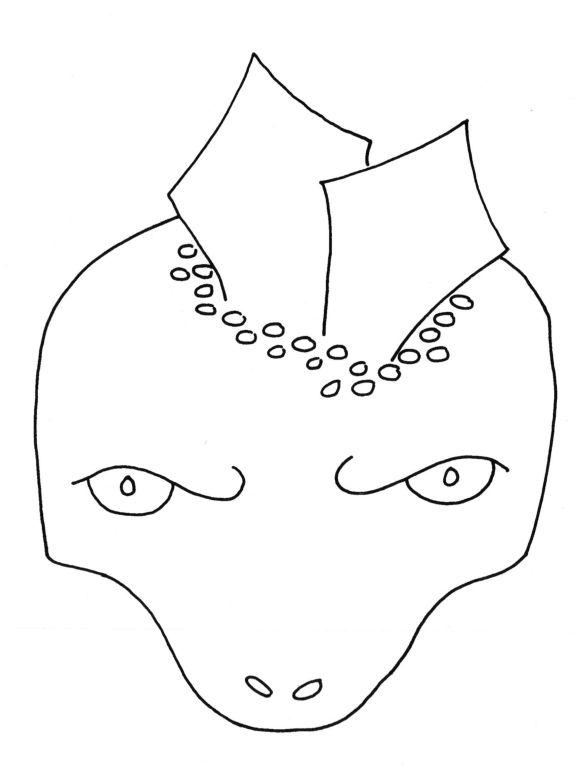

STAN STEGOSAURUS PUPPET PATTERN

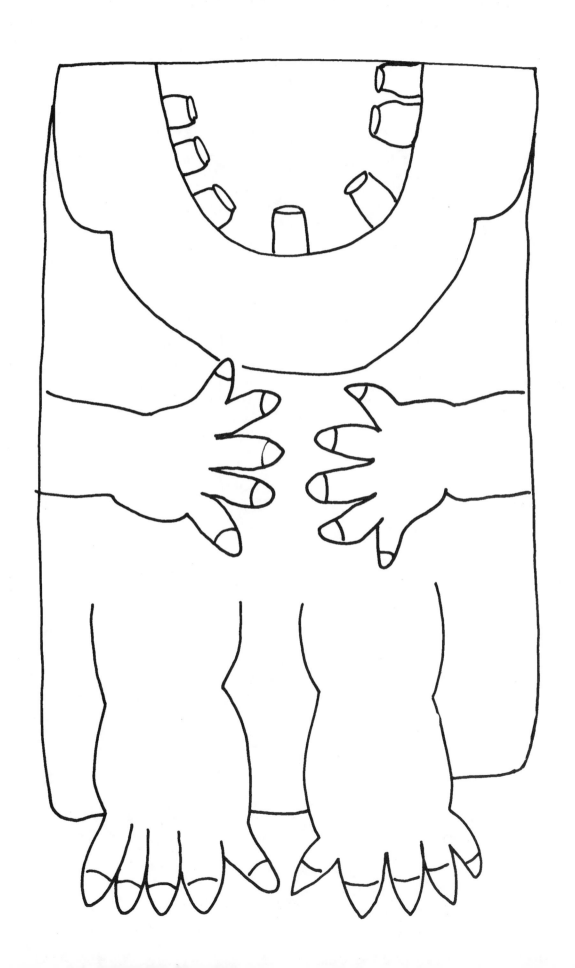

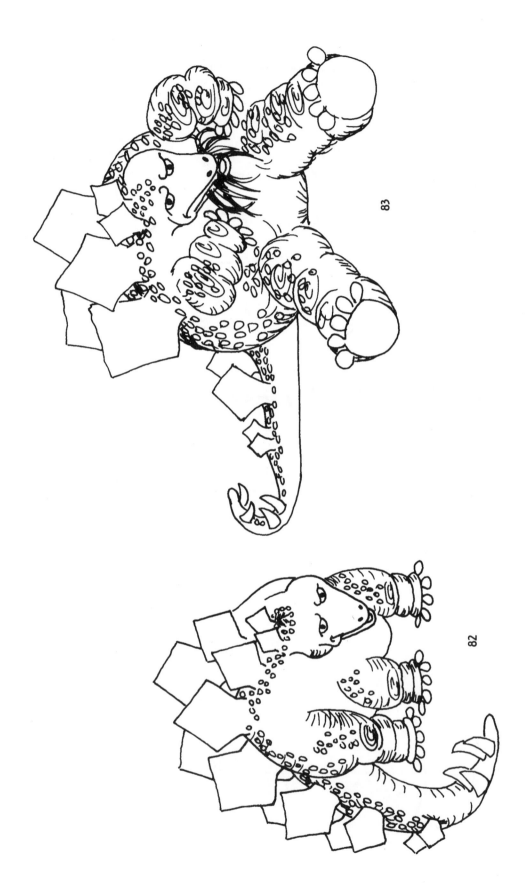

83

82

SWAMP SWIMMER

FLANNEL BOARD STORY

(figure 84) Deep in the sweltering swamp lives Swamp Swimmer. He is not sweet; he is an alligator. You'd sometimes swear he's a log being swept slowly down stream. *(figure 85)* In one swift swirl he could prove you wrong.

If you're ever in the swamp, keep an eye out for Swamp Swimmer.

SWAMP SWIMMER SONG

(Can be sung to "The Wheels on the Bus")

The eyes of Swamp Swimmer
Go blink, blink, blink,
Blink, blink, blink,
Blink, blink, blink.
The eyes of Swamp Swimmer go
Blink, blink, blink
All through the swamp.

The tail of Swamp Swimmer
Goes swish, swish, swish,
Swish, swish, swish,
Swish, swish, swish.
The tail of Swamp Swimmer
Goes swish, swish, swish
All through the swamp.

The teeth of Swamp Swimmer
Go snap, snap, snap,
Snap, snap, snap,
Snap, snap, snap.
The teeth of Swamp Swimmer
Go snap, snap, snap
All through the swamp.

VOCABULARY

Initial /sw/

ONE-SYLLABLE WORDS

<u>suave</u>	<u>swamp</u>	<u>sway</u>	swept	switch
<u>suede</u>	swan	swear	<u>swift</u>	swoon
suite	<u>swap</u>	sweat	<u>swim</u>	<u>swoop</u>
swab	<u>swarm</u>	<u>sweep</u>	swine	swore
swag	<u>swat</u>	<u>sweet</u>	swing	sworn
swam	swatch	swell	swirl	

TWO-SYLLABLE WORDS

<u>swallow</u>	sweeten	swelling	swimmer
sweater	sweetheart	<u>swelter</u>	<u>swindle</u>
sweepstakes			

SWAMP SWIMMER PUPPET

Materials:

green construction paper;

yellow, white, green, and black crayons;

lunch bag;

scissors;

glue

Directions:

1. Duplicate the patterns on construction paper.

2. Outline eyes and nostrils with black. Fill in the "eyeliner" on side of eyes with black and fill in pupils and nostrils with black. Fill in inside of mouth (top and bottom) with black. Color the teeth white. Color the eyes yellow. Outline the rest of the puppet with dark green. Using the same crayon, make scales all over the body and on the outside of the head.

3. Cut out all pieces. Glue on body. Glue on head. Put glue on the bag and fit the top so it matches the mouth part of the body correctly. Glue the inside of the mouth to the top of the inside of the head, going all the way to the crease.

PARENT MEMO

Today's date: _____

Child's name: _____

Dear Parent:

Please set aside five minutes a day to work on these exercises for initial /sw/.

Please read these words to your child every day. Your child is to listen, but not repeat them to you.

suave	swamp	swat	sweet	swindle
suede	swap	sway	swelter	swim
swallow	swarm	sweep	swift	swoop

Your child should practice saying these each day. Check off each time he or she says the words to you.

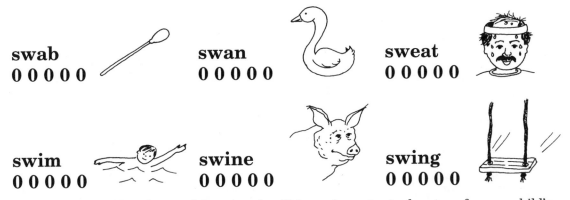

swab
O O O O O

swan
O O O O O

sweat
O O O O O

swim
O O O O O

swine
O O O O O

swing
O O O O O

Helping your child with speech homework will be an important advantage for your child's progress. If your child experiences difficulty or frustration, stop. Try to make your sessions brief and positive. If you want to further enrich your child's speech program and language development, you might consider checking out any of the following books from the library and reading them with your child. They contain initial /sw/ in the titles.

Swimmy by Leo Lionni
The Swineherd by Hans Christian Andersen

Songs you can sing emphasizing initial /sw/ are "Swing Low, Sweet Chariot" and "Would You Like to Swing on a Star?"

Thank you for your support. Please sign and return this when you have completed the above lessons.

Additional Teacher Comment *(optional):*

Parent signature _____

Please write your comments, if any, on the back of this memo.

SWAMP SWIMMER ACTIVITY PAGE

Look carefully! Color the pictures that begin with /sw/.

SWAMP SWIMMER PUPPET PATTERN

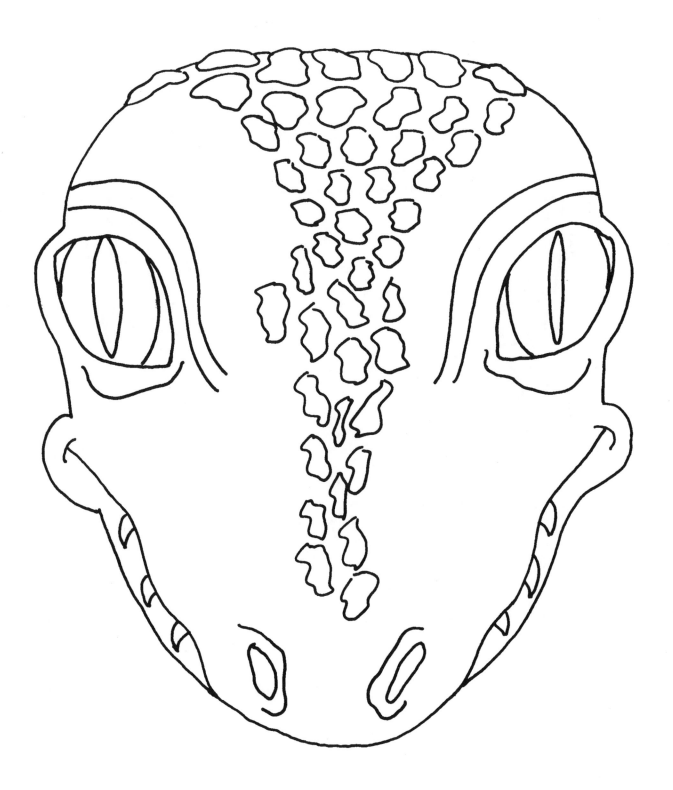

SWAMP SWIMMER PUPPET PATTERN

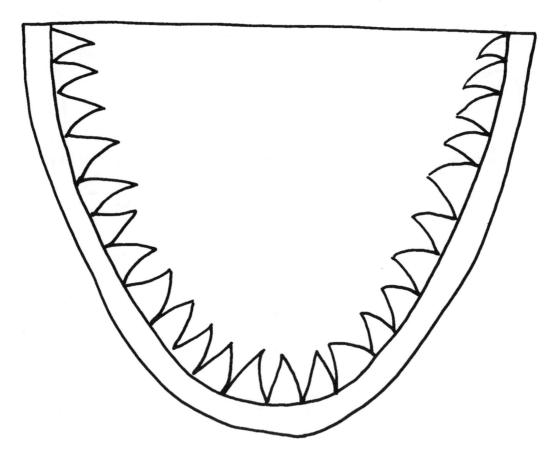

MOUTH TOP

SWAMP SWIMMER PUPPET PATTERN

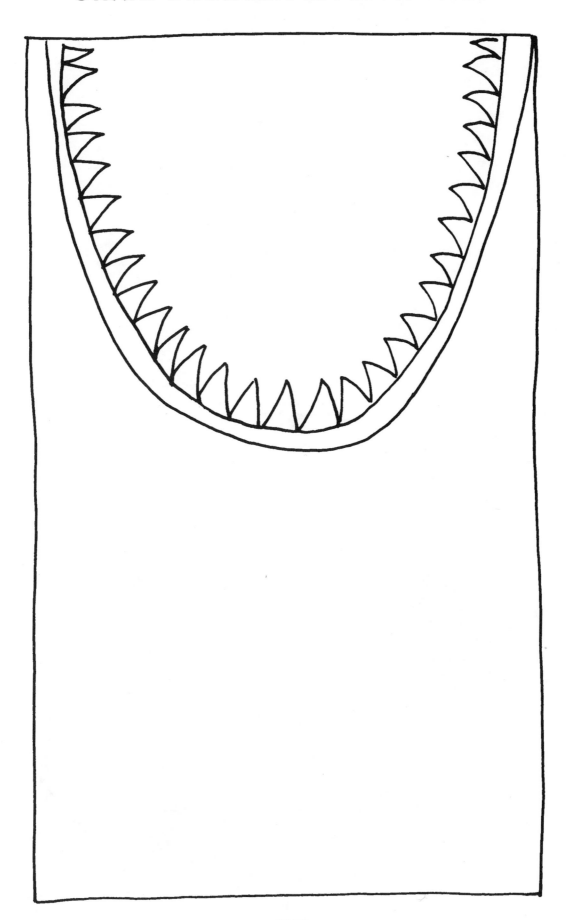

GREEN

85

84

THEO THOROUGHBRED

FLANNEL BOARD STORY

Theo Thoroughbred was thrilled. *(figure 86)* One Thursday the thermometer said thirty degrees. The snow was going to thaw. Theo had thought a thousand times of Spring and now he knew it was coming soon. More than anything, Theo knew his dream of thick green grass would come true. He was so thankful!

THEO THOROUGHBRED SONG

(Can be sung to "A Hunting We Will Go")

I think of Spring, you know.
The thick green grass will grow.
It's one, two, three and off I'll be
To where the thick grass grows.
Thank goodness for Springtime and thick grass
And where the thick grass grows.

VOCABULARY

Initial /th/

ONE-SYLLABLE WORDS

thank	theme	thin	thirst	thud
thatch	thick	thing	thorn	thumb
thaw	thigh	third	thought	thump
theft				

TWO-SYLLABLE WORDS

thankful	thinker	thistle	thoughtful	thunder
thicken	thirteen	thorough	thousand	Thursday
thimble	thirty			

THEO THOROUGHBRED PUPPET

Materials:

brown construction paper;

black, white, and brown crayons;

lunch bag;

scissors;

glue

Directions:

1. Duplicate the patterns on construction paper.

2. Outline the horse in black. Color inside of ears, mane, nostrils, inside of mouth, and pupils of eyes black. Color teeth white. Color eyes brown. Color bottom lip brown.

3. Cut out and glue on bag.

PARENT MEMO

Today's date: _____

Child's name: _____

Dear Parent:

Please set aside five minutes a day to work on these exercises for initial /th/.

Please read these words to your child every day. Your child is to listen, but not repeat them to you.

thank	theme	thing	thorn	thumb
thaw	thick	third	thought	thunder
theft	thin	thirst	thud	Thursday

Your child should practice saying these each day. Check off each time he or she says the words to you.

thank
0 0 0 0 0

thaw
0 0 0 0 0

theft
0 0 0 0 0

thigh
0 0 0 0 0

thin
0 0 0 0 0

thumb
0 0 0 0 0

Helping your child with speech homework will be an important advantage for your child's progress. If your child experiences difficulty or frustration, stop. Try to make your sessions brief and positive. If you want to further enrich your child's speech program and language development, you might consider checking out any of the following books from the library and reading them with your child. They contain initial /th/ in the titles.

I Never Say I'm Thankful, But I Am by Jane B. Moncure
Thumbelina by Hans Christian Andersen

Singing "Where Is Thumbkin?" with your child is another way to emphasize the initial /th/ sound.

Thank you for your support. Please sign and return this when you have completed the above lessons.

Additional Teacher Comment *(optional):*

Parent signature _____

Please write your comments, if any, on the back of this memo.

THEO THOROUGHBRED ACTIVITY PAGE

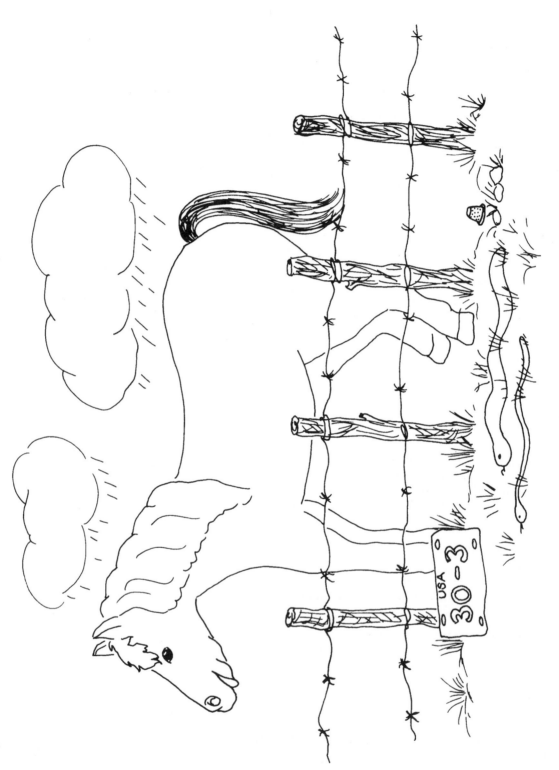

Color the objects that begin with /th/.

©1996 by Elizabeth Krepelin and Bonnie Mae Smith

312

THEO THOROUGHBRED PUPPET PATTERN

THEO THOROUGHBRED PUPPET PATTERN

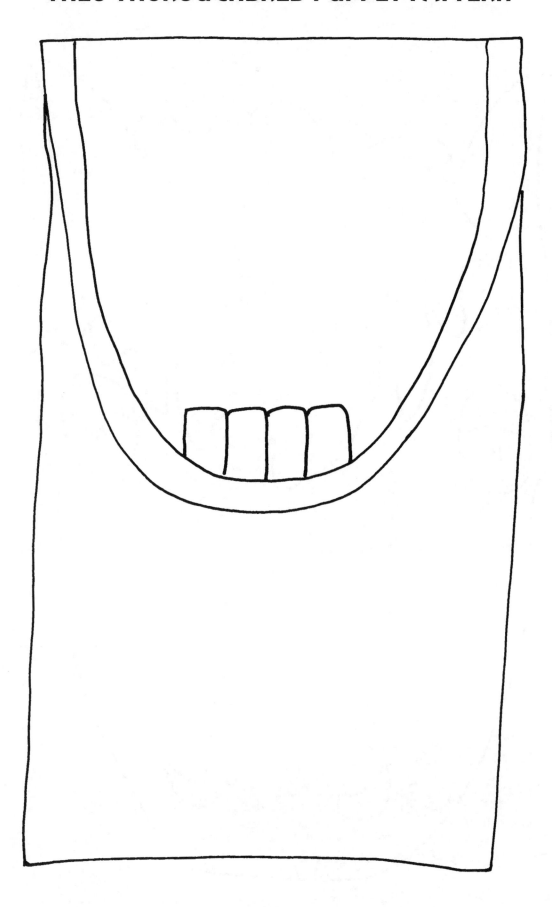

THEO THOROUGHBRED B&W FLANNEL BOARD FIGURE

86

TROY TRICERATOPS

FLANNEL BOARD STORY

(figure 87) Troy Triceratops trod the earth trimming trees and trampling about many, many years ago. He was tremendous in size; bigger than a truck or a train on a track. When he traveled, the earth trembled. He came to a tragic end, not a triumph.

(figure 88) To tell the truth, if the triceratops lived now, there would be trouble. He would truly stop traffic wherever he would tread. Surely he would trample everything in his travels. Someone would have to trick him into a trap and transplant him far away.

TROY TRICERATOPS SONG

(Can be sung to "The Eensy Weensy Spider")

Tremendous Troy Triceratops could trample on a train,
Could trash entire countries and drive us all insane.
The earth would shake and tremble and trouble would abound.
Truth to tell, it's lucky that Troy cannot be found!

VOCABULARY

Initial /tr/

ONE-SYLLABLE WORDS

trace	trance	trench	trod	trump
track	trap	trend	troll	trunk
trade	trash	tribe	troop	trust
trail	tray	trick	trot	truth
train	tread	trill	trout	try
trait	treat	trim	truck	
tramp	tree	trite	true	

TWO-SYLLABLE WORDS

tractor	tranquil	treadmill	trickle	triple
trademark	transfer	treasure	tricky	trolley
traffic	transpire	trellis	trigger	trombone
tragic	transplant	tremble	trillion	trophy
trailer	trapeze	trespass	trinket	trouble
trample	travel	tribute	trio	trousers

TROY TRICERATOPS PUPPET

Although this puppet can be done on lavender or green construction paper, it is really fun to do it on white construction paper. Do tracing and coloring hard and waxy. Use a watery tempera or watercolor wash. Green, turquoise, purple, or peach would make interesting washes. This creates a crayon resist.

Materials:

Choose either a colored or white construction paper;

black, yellow, white, and peach crayons;

watery tempera paint and a brush if you choose to do the crayon resist;

lunch bag;

scissors;

glue

Directions:

1. Duplicate the patterns on construction paper.

2. Press hard with crayon. Outline entire figure with black. Fill in eyes and mouth with black. Fill in teeth with yellow. Fill in horns and nails with peach, if available.

3. Cut out and glue onto bag. Quickly wash with watery tempera. Let dry.

PARENT MEMO

Today's date: _____

Child's name: _____

Dear Parent:

Please set aside five minutes a day to work on these exercises for initial /tr/.

Please read these words to your child every day. Your child is to listen, but not repeat them to you.

trace	trail	trap	tree	troop
track	train	trash	tribe	trouble
tractor	tramp	treat	trick	trust

Your child should practice saying these each day. Check off each time he or she says the words to you.

train
0 0 0 0 0

trap
0 0 0 0 0

trash
0 0 0 0 0

tree
0 0 0 0 0

truck
0 0 0 0 0

trunk
0 0 0 0 0

Helping your child with speech homework will be an important advantage for your child's progress. If your child experiences difficulty or frustration, stop. Try to make your sessions brief and positive. If you want to further enrich your child's speech program and language development, you might consider checking out any of the following books from the library and reading them with your child. They contain initial /tr/ in the titles.

Little Bear's Trousers by Jane Hissey
The Giving Tree by Shel Silverstein
The True Story of the Three Little Pigs by Jon Scieszka
Trouble with Trolls by Jan Brett

Thank you for your support. Please sign and return this when you have completed the above lessons.

Additional Teacher Comment *(optional):*

Parent signature _____

Please write your comments, if any, on the back of this memo.

TROY TRICERATOPS ACTIVITY PAGE

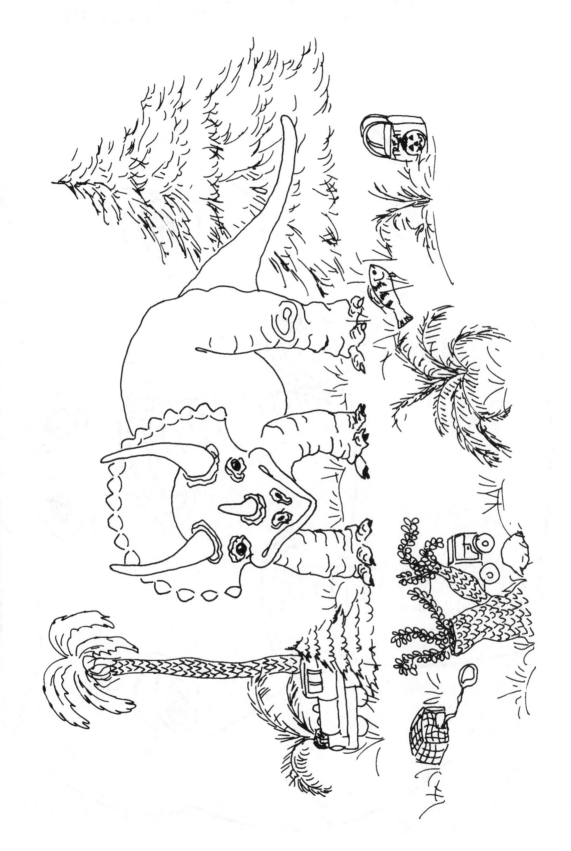

Color the pictures that begin with /tr/.

TROY TRICERATOPS PUPPET PATTERN

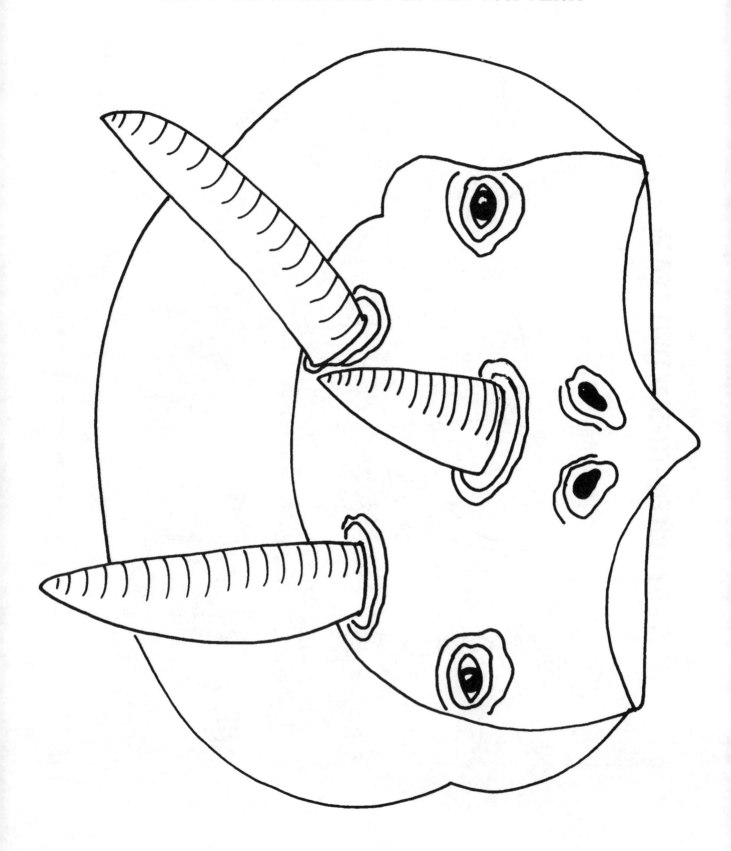

TROY TRICERATOPS PUPPET PATTERN

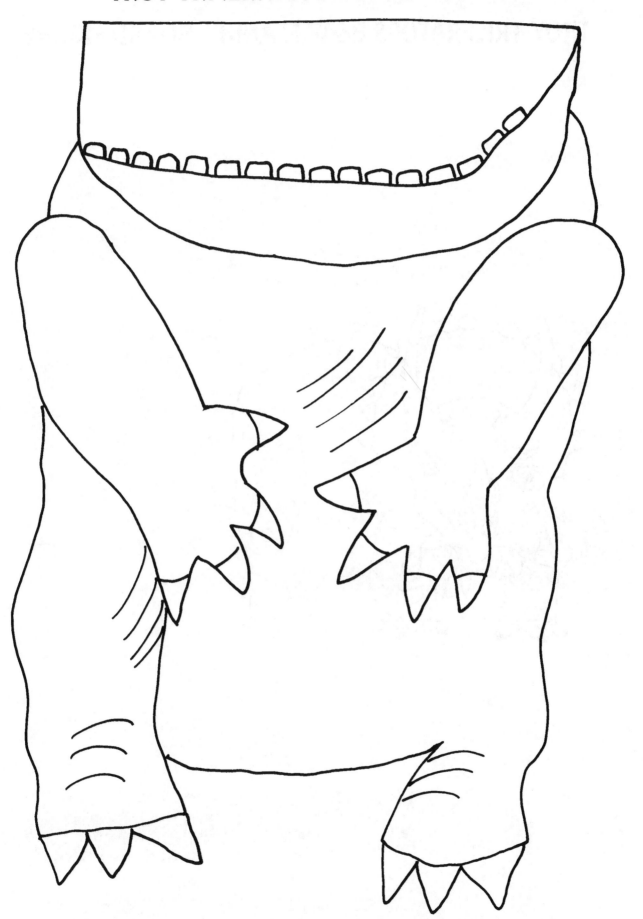

TROY TRICERATOPS B&W FLANNEL BOARD FIGURE

87

TROY TRICERATOPS B&W FLANNEL BOARD FIGURE

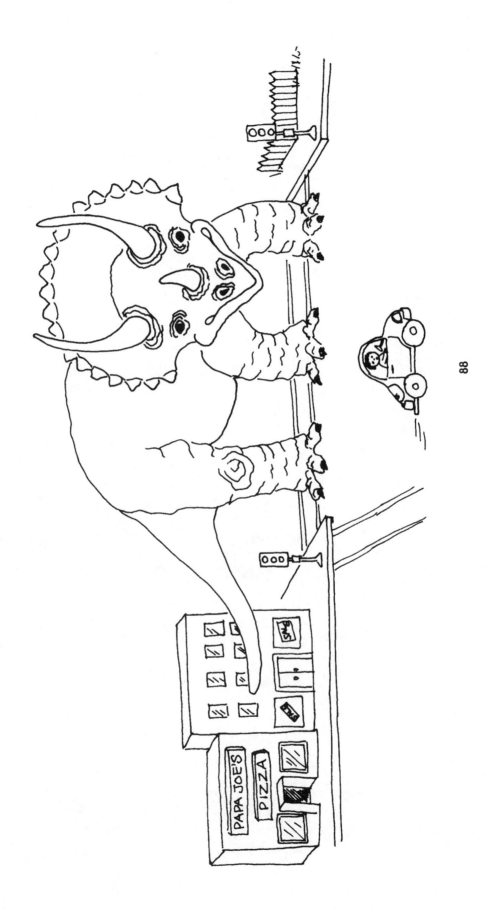

88

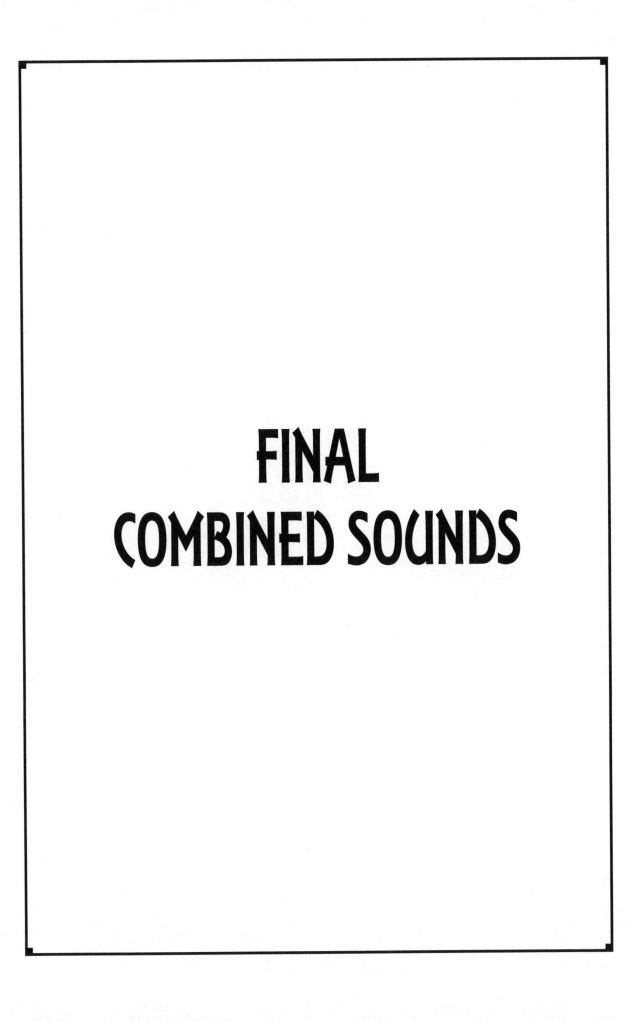

FINAL
COMBINED SOUNDS

SWISH FISH

FLANNEL BOARD STORY

(figure 89) Swish is a magic Fish that lives in the lush sea near an island with the silly name of Mustache. Swish is a fish to cherish because she can grant you a wish.

    She loves to splash in the sea. If you are foolish enough to rush in and try to catch her, she will never come to you. *(figure 90)* But if you refresh yourself in the water, and if Swish knows you are an unselfish person who lives with relish, she might brush past you and with a flourish, grant you a wish.

SWISH FISH SONG

(Can be sung to "Twinkle, Twinkle, Little Star")

Swish, Swish, magic fish,
How I'd love to have a wish.

Please splash by and swish your fin,
Make my dreams come true and win.

Swish, Swish, magic fish,
How I'd love to have a wish.

VOCABULARY

Final /sh/

ONE-SYLLABLE WORDS

ash	<u>dash</u>	gush	plush	splash
bash	dish	hash	<u>push</u>	squash
<u>blush</u>	fish	<u>hush</u>	rash	squish
<u>brush</u>	<u>flash</u>	lash	<u>rush</u>	swish
bush	<u>flesh</u>	leash	slash	thrash
<u>cash</u>	flush	lush	slosh	<u>trash</u>
clash	fresh	mash	slush	wash
<u>crash</u>	gash	mesh	smash	<u>wish</u>
<u>crush</u>	gosh	mush		

TWO-SYLLABLE WORDS

backlash	childish	foolish	punish	sluggish
banish	eyelash	furnish	radish	tarnish
blemish	famish	mustache	refresh	vanquish
burnish	finish	nourish	relish	varnish
cherish	flourish	polish	selfish	

SWISH FISH PUPPET

Materials:

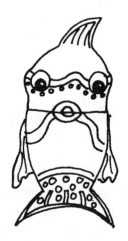

bright colored construction paper;

black crayon;

various bright colors of tempera paint;

cotton swabs;

lunch bag;

scissors;

glue

Directions:

1. Duplicate the patterns on construction paper. Cut off five inches from the bottom of the bag.

2. Trace all parts with black crayon. Fill in eyes with black.

3. Cut out and glue onto bag. Using cotton swabs like paint brushes, paint the fish with various colors of tempera paint. To create scales, dip fingertip into paint and print fingerprint-like scales.

PARENT MEMO

Today's date: _____

Child's name: _____

Dear Parent:

Please set aside five minutes a day to work on these exercises for final /sh/.

Please read these words to your child every day. Your child is to listen, but not repeat them to you.

blush	crash	flash	mustache	rush
brush	crush	flesh	push	trash
cash	dash	hush	radish	wish

Your child should practice saying these each day. Check off each time he or she says the words to you.

brush
O O O O O

bush
O O O O O

dish
O O O O O

fish
O O O O O

leash
O O O O O

trash
O O O O O

Helping your child with speech homework will be an important advantage for your child's progress. If your child experiences difficulty or frustration, stop. Try to make your sessions brief and positive. If you want to further enrich your child's speech program and language development, you might consider checking out any of the following books from the library and reading them with your child. They contain final /sh/ in the titles.

Flash, Crash, Rumble and Roll revised by Franklyn M. Branley
Go and Hush the Baby by Betsy C. Byars
One Fish, Two Fish, Red Fish, Blue Fish by Dr. Seuss
Rainbow Fish by Marcus Pfister

Songs you can sing emphasizing final /sh/ are "Hush Little Baby Don't Say a Word," "Here We Go Round the Mulberry Bush," and "Splish, Splash."

Thank you for your support. Please sign and return this when you have completed the above lessons.

Additional Teacher Comment *(optional):*

Parent signature _____

Please write any comments, if any, on the back of this memo.

SWISH FISH ACTIVITY PAGE

Circle the pictures that end in /sh/.

SWISH FISH PUPPET PATTERN

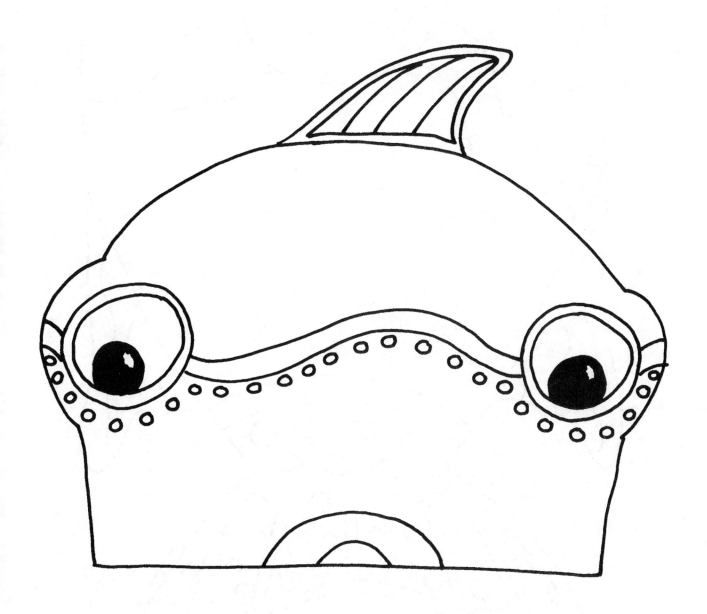

SWISH FISH PUPPET PATTERN

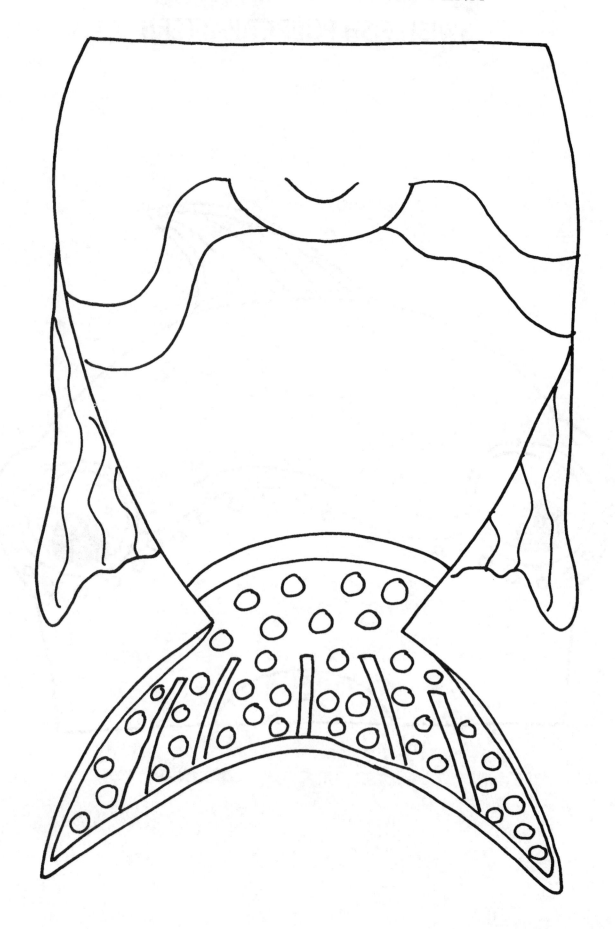

SWISH FISH B&W FLANNEL BOARD FIGURES

89

90

BLANCHE OSTRICH

FLANNEL BOARD STORY

(figure 91) Blanche Ostrich could teach you about running. She'd be a great coach. No one can catch her. She's fun to watch as she heads for the home stretch.

(figure 92) If you could hitch a wagon to her, she'd fetch you a fast ride. She can't fly like other birds, but she's the fastest runner of the bunch.

BLANCHE OSTRICH SONG

(Can be sung to "Did You Ever See a Lassie?")

Did you ever see an ostrich,
An ostrich, an ostrich,
Did you ever see an ostrich run fast in a race?

It's such a fast runner,
You can't catch this stunner.
Did you ever see an ostrich run fast in a race?

VOCABULARY

Final /ch/

ONE-SYLLABLE WORDS

batch	clutch	hitch	pouch	splotch
beach	cinch	itch	preach	stitch
bench	coach	latch	quench	such
bleach	couch	lunch	ranch	switch
blotch	crunch	match	reach	teach
branch	crutch	much	rich	touch
breach	ditch	notch	scratch	trench
broach	each	patch	screech	watch
brunch	fetch	peach	sketch	witch
bunch	grouch	pitch	slouch	
catch	hatch	pooch	speech	

TWO-SYLLABLE WORDS

approach	cockroach	enrich	ostrich	topnotch
bewitch	detach	hopscotch	sandwich	

BLANCHE OSTRICH PUPPET

Materials:

gray and black construction paper;

pink (or orange), brown, and black crayons;

lunch bag;

scissors;

glue

Directions:

1. Duplicate the patterns on construction paper.

2. Outline entire puppet in black. Color inside of mouth black. Color pupils of eyes and nostrils black. Color beak and bottom "lip" pink. (If pink is not available, orange would look fine.) Color eyes brown.

3. Cut out all parts. Glue head to flap. Glue neck to bag, lining up with beak. Glue on black body. Glue legs to front of body.

PARENT MEMO

Today's date: _____

Child's name: _____

Dear Parent:

Please set aside five minutes a day to work on these exercises for final /ch/.

Please read these words to your child every day. Your child is to listen, but not repeat them to you.

beach	bunch	each	itch	pooch
bleach	cinch	grouch	much	quench
branch	coach	hatch	patch	screech

Your child should practice saying these each day. Check off each time he or she says the words to you.

beach
O O O O O

branch
O O O O O

couch
O O O O O

crutch
O O O O O

match
O O O O O

peach
O O O O O

Helping your child with speech homework will be an important advantage for your child's progress. If your child experiences difficulty or frustration, stop. Try to make your sessions brief and positive. If you want to further enrich your child's speech program and language development, you might consider checking out any of the following books from the library and reading them with your child. They contain final /ch/ in the titles.

James and the Giant Peach by Roald Dahl
Tar Beach by Faith Ringgold
The Giant Jam Sandwich by John V. Lord and Janet Burroway

Thank you for your support. Please sign and return this when you have completed the above lessons.

Additional Teacher Comment *(optional):*

Parent signature _____

Please write any comments, if any, on the back of this memo.

BLANCHE OSTRICH ACTIVITY PAGE

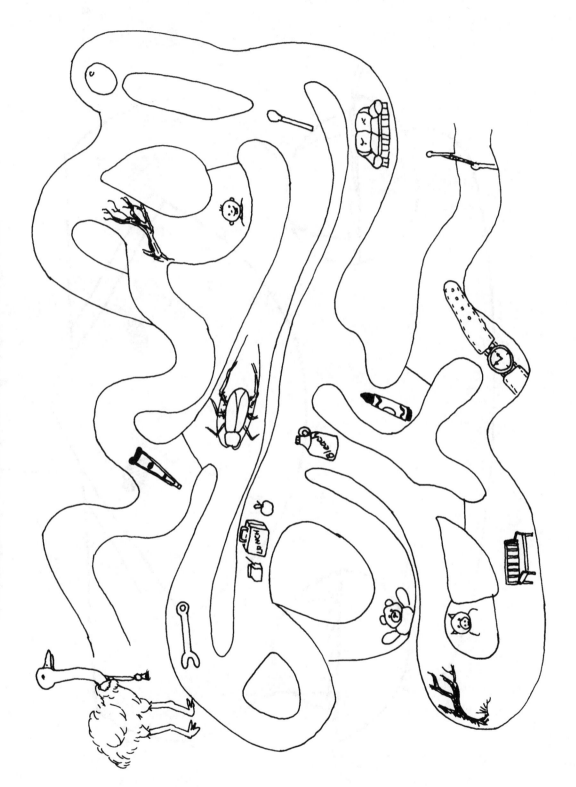

Color the pictures that end in /ch/ to help Blanche reach the end of the race.

BLANCHE OSTRICH PUPPET PATTERN

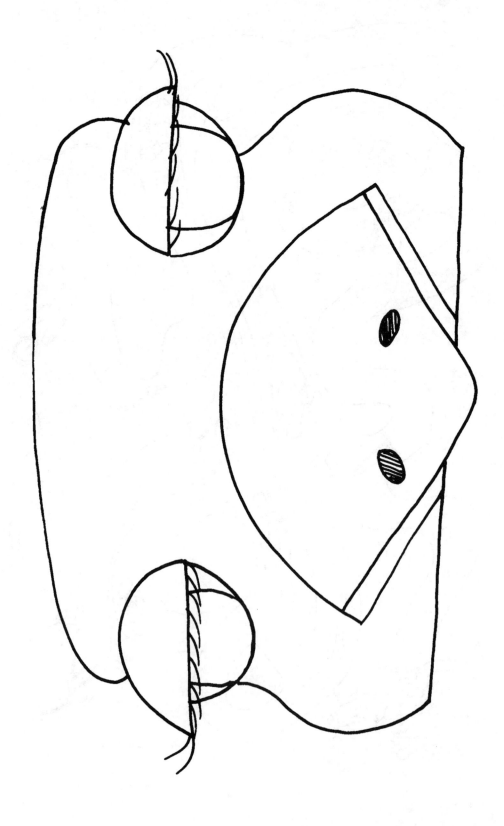

BLANCHE OSTRICH PUPPET PATTERN

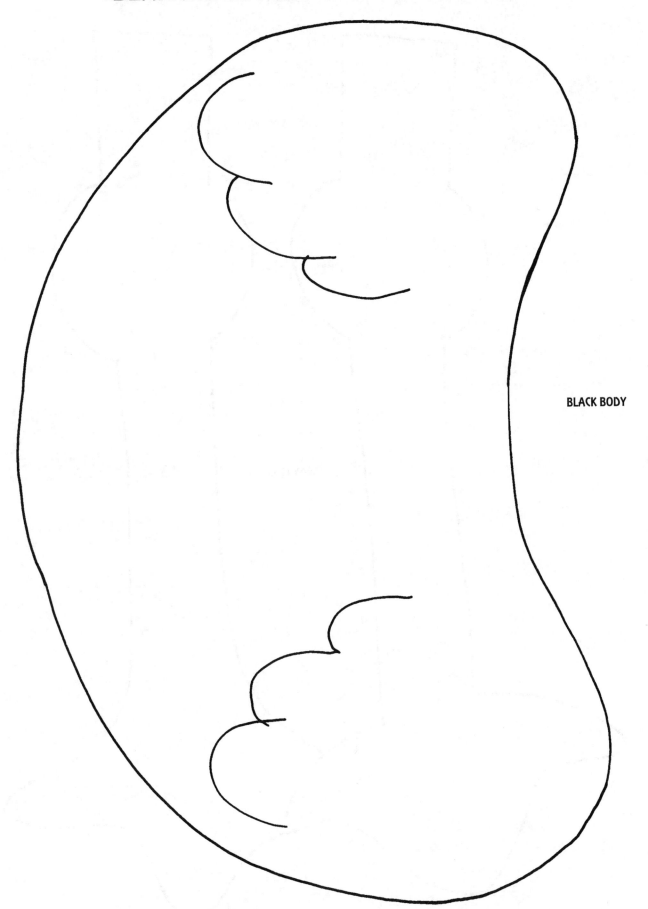

BLACK BODY

BLANCHE OSTRICH PUPPET PATTERNS

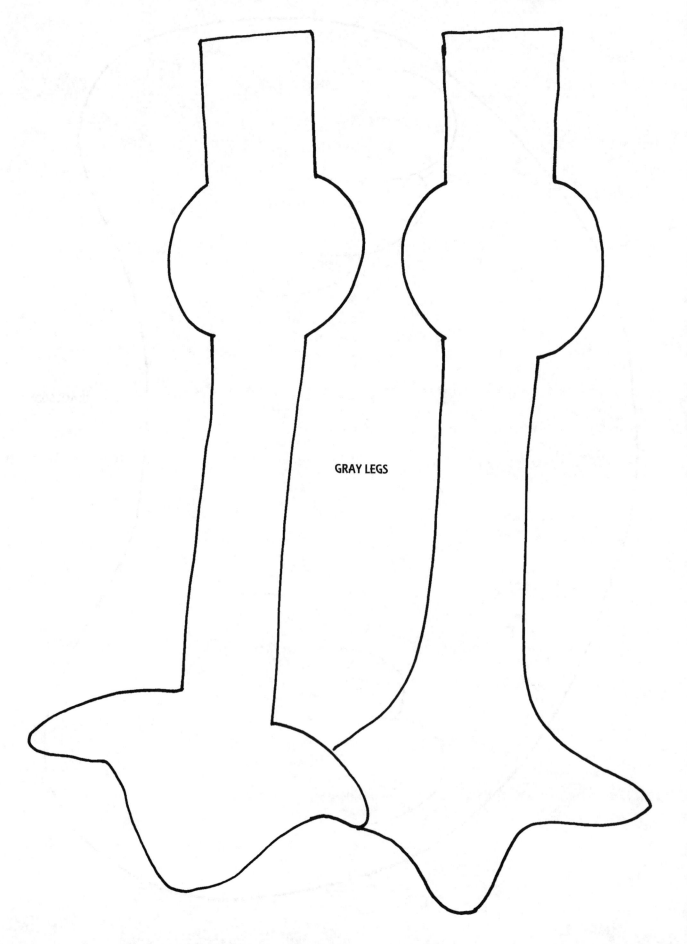

GRAY LEGS

BLANCHE OSTRICH PUPPET PATTERN

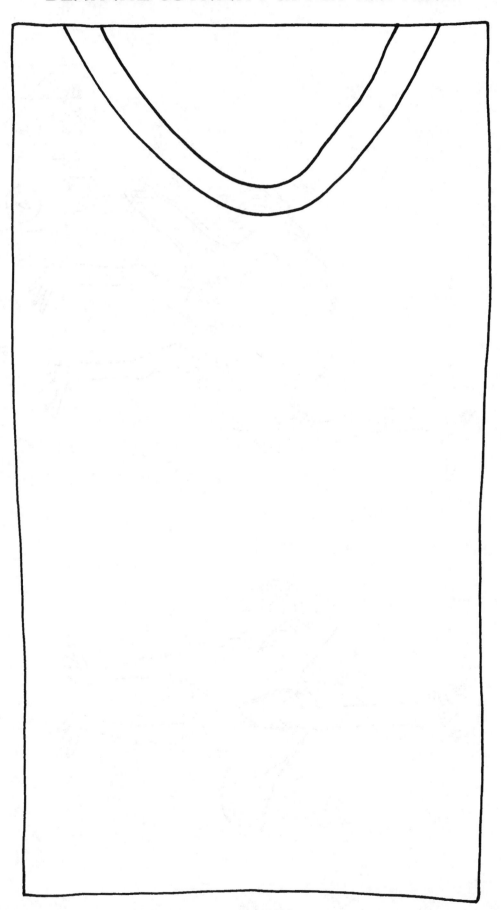

GRAY BODY

BLANCHE OSTRICH B&W FLANNEL BOARD FIGURES

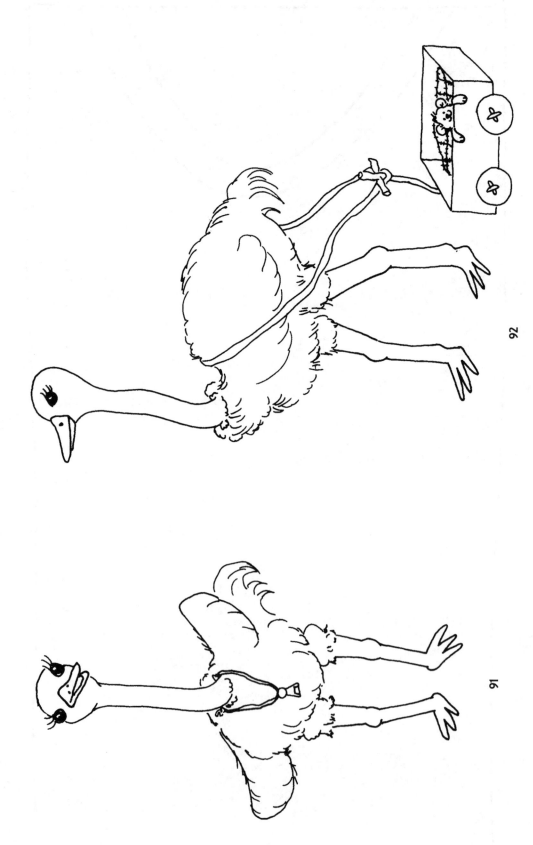

92

91

COLOR TOPS

FLANNEL BOARD STORY

Look at the color tops spin! *(figure 93)* Black, *(figure 94)* red, *(figure 95)* green, *(figure 96)* orange, *(figure 97)* brown, *(figure 98)* yellow, *(figure 99)* purple, and *(figure 100)* blue. Can you choose the color top that answers these riddles?

All tops remain on the flannel board. The teacher gives the clues and the student chooses the top that answers the riddle.

I am the color of the sky when the city sleeps.

I am the color of the sea on maps.

I am the color of grapes and violets.

I am the color of the jack-o'-lantern with big eyes, nose, and lips.

Give me two scoops of the color of chocolate.

I am the color of sunshine and tulips.

I am the color of the tops of trees.

I am the color of the stripes on our American flag.

VOCABULARY

Final /ps/

ONE-SYLLABLE WORDS

apes	cups	lips	scrapes	<u>stripes</u>
<u>beeps</u>	drapes	<u>maps</u>	shapes	sweeps
bops	drips	mops	ships	<u>tops</u>
caps	droops	naps	skips	traps
<u>capes</u>	grapes	<u>plops</u>	slaps	trips
chips	heaps	props	<u>sleeps</u>	types
chops	<u>hops</u>	pups	slips	<u>whips</u>
claps	hopes	<u>raps</u>	snaps	wipes
clips	<u>keeps</u>	<u>rips</u>	steps	wraps
creeps	leaps	scoops	stops	<u>zaps</u>

TWO-SYLLABLE WORDS

bagpipes	<u>escapes</u>	gallops	scallops	<u>tulips</u>
bebop	footsteps	gumdrops	teacups	worships

COLOR TOPS STICK PUPPETS

Materials:

construction paper;

craft sticks;

crayons or markers;

scissors;

glue

Directions:

1. These stick puppets can be made using the top patterns. Duplicate the patterns on construction paper.

2. Trace, color, and cut out. Glue each one to the end of a craft stick. (Or have the children draw their own tops and turn them into stick puppets.)

3. Students can make up riddles similar to the flannel board riddles. They can either say them, dictate them, or write the riddles depending on ability level and therapist discretion.

PARENT MEMO

Today's date: _____

Child's name: _____

Dear Parent:

Please set aside five minutes a day to work on these exercises for final /ps/.

Please read these words to your child every day. Your child is to listen, but not repeat them to you.

beeps	hops	plops	sleeps	tulips
capes	keeps	raps	stripes	whips
escapes	maps	rips	tops	zaps

Your child should practice saying these each day. Check off each time he or she says the words to you.

caps
0 0 0 0 0

chips
0 0 0 0 0

cups
0 0 0 0 0

grapes
0 0 0 0 0

lips
0 0 0 0 0

shapes
0 0 0 0 0

Helping your child with speech homework will be an important advantage for your child's progress. If your child experiences difficulty or frustration, stop. Try to make your sessions brief and positive.

Thank you for your support. Please sign and return this when you have completed the above lessons.

Additional Teacher Comment *(optional)*:

Parent signature _____

Please write any comments, if any, on the back of this memo.

COLOR TOPS B&W FLANNEL BOARD FIGURES

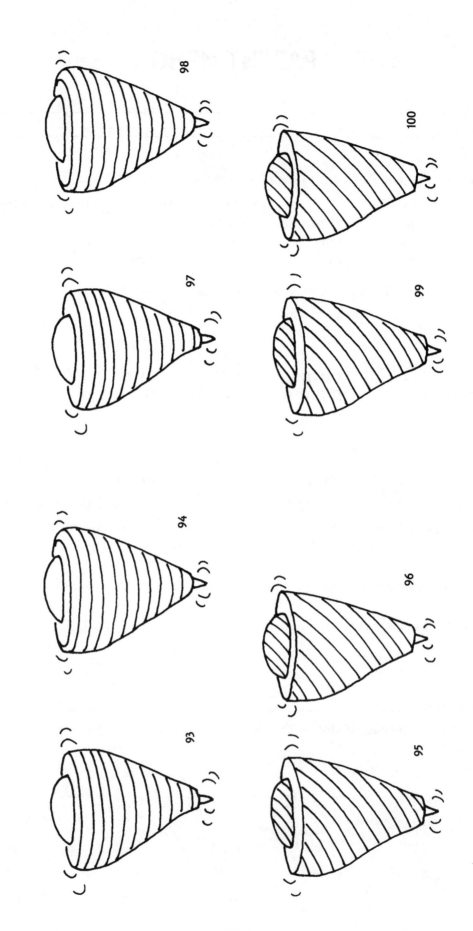

©1996 by Elizabeth Krepelin and Bonnie Mae Smith

BUILDING BLOCKS

FLANNEL BOARD STORY

(figure 101, point to shapes in figure as you read the story) Here are building blocks. They can be used to build many things. You can see a circle in the blocks and a triangle and a rectangle and a square. See if you can solve these building block riddles.

    Let the student put the correct block shape in the missing spot and solve the riddle.

(figure 102) Wheels on bikes are this shape.

(figure 103) Beaks on hawks are this shape.

(figure 104) Books can be this shape.

(figure 105) Bricks are this shape.

VOCABULARY

Final /cks/

ONE-SYLLABLE WORDS

aches	chokes	hooks	pokes	snakes
bakes	clocks	jokes	quacks	sneaks
beaks	clucks	leaks	racks	soaks
bikes	cooks	locks	rakes	socks
blocks	croaks	likes	rocks	speaks
books	decks	looks	sacks	strikes
breaks	ducks	makes	seeks	takes
bricks	fakes	necks	shakes	talks
brooks	flicks	pecks	shocks	tricks
bucks	folks	peeks	smacks	trucks
cakes	frocks	picks	smokes	weeks
chalks	hawks	plucks	snacks	yolks
checks	hikes			
chicks				

TWO-SYLLABLE WORDS

attacks	cupcakes	panics	sweepstakes	toothpicks
chopsticks	frolics			

BUILDING BLOCKS STICK PUPPETS

Materials:

construction paper;

craft sticks;

crayons or markers;

scissors;

glue

Directions:

1. These stick puppets can be made using the shape patterns. Duplicate the patterns on construction paper.

2. Trace, color, and cut out. Glue each one to the end of a craft stick.

3. Students can make up riddles similar to the flannel board riddles. They can either say them, dictate them, or write the riddles depending on ability level and therapist discretion.

PARENT MEMO

Today's date: _____

Child's name: _____

Dear Parent:

Please set aside five minutes a day to work on these exercises for final /cks/.

Please read these words to your child every day. Your child is to listen, but not repeat them to you.

beaks	cooks	quacks	sneaks	sweepstakes
bikes	croaks	shakes	speaks	takes
brooks	peeks	snacks	strikes	toothpicks

Your child should practice saying these each day. Check off each time he or she says the words to you.

books
0 0 0 0 0

cakes
0 0 0 0 0

chicks
0 0 0 0 0

ducks
0 0 0 0 0

hooks
0 0 0 0 0

snakes
0 0 0 0 0

Helping your child with speech homework will be an important advantage for your child's progress. If your child experiences difficulty or frustration, stop. Try to make your sessions brief and positive.

Thank you for your support. Please sign and return this when you have completed the above lessons.

Additional Teacher Comment *(optional)*:

Parent signature _____

Please write any comments, if any, on the back of this memo.

BUILDING BLOCKS B&W FLANNEL BOARD FIGURES

101

102

103

104

105

HAPPY HATS

FLANNEL BOARD STORY

There are many kinds of hats that people wear for different reasons. Some hats protect your head. *(figure 106)* Some just look pretty *(figure 107)* or handsome. *(figure 108)* See if you can guess who these happy hats belong to.

Teacher displays the hat on the flannel board and student guesses from the clue to whom the hat belongs.

(figure 109) I make sweets that are treats like doughnuts and cookies.

(figure 110) I'm the one who greets you at the circus and plots to make you laugh.

(figure 111) My friends are bats and black cats.

(figure 112) You usually see me in December. I wear a red suit and boots.

VOCABULARY

Final /ts/

ONE-SYLLABLE WORDS

bats	dots	hats	oats	snouts
belts	doubts	hits	pats	spits
bets	eats	hoots	pets	splits
bits	fights	jets	plates	states
bites	fits	kites	rats	streets
boats	flits	knights	roots	swats
boots	floats	knits	scoots	sweats
cats	frets	lights	seats	sweets
chats	fruits	meats	shots	thoughts
cleats	gates	mutts	shouts	tots
coats	gets	nets	skates	treats
cots	goats	notes	skits	votes
crates	greets	nuts	slats	waits
cats				
dates				

TWO-SYLLABLE WORDS

athletes	closets	habits	peanuts	rockets
awaits	creates	lockets	pockets	sunsets
baskets	donates	markets	poets	upsets
bonnets	doughnuts	minutes	rabbits	wallets
bracelets	forgets	parrots	robots	

HAPPY HATS STICK PUPPETS

Materials:

construction paper;

craft sticks;

crayons or markers;

scissors;

glue

Directions:

1. These stick puppets can be made using the hat patterns. Duplicate the patterns on construction paper.

2. Trace, color, and cut out. Glue each one to the end of a craft stick. (Or have the children draw their own hats and turn them into stick puppets.)

3. Students can make up riddles similar to the flannel board riddles. They can either say them, dictate them, or write the riddles depending on ability level and therapist discretion.

PARENT MEMO

Today's date: _____

Child's name: _____

Dear Parent:

Please set aside five minutes a day to work on these exercises for final /ts/.

Please read these words to your child every day. Your child is to listen, but not repeat them to you.

bets	cuts	floats	pats	sweets
bites	eats	frets	pets	tots
boots	flits	fruits	shouts	treats

Your child should practice saying these each day. Check off each time he or she says the words to you.

bats
0 0 0 0 0

boats
0 0 0 0 0

cats
0 0 0 0 0

fruits
0 0 0 0 0

pets
0 0 0 0 0

skates
0 0 0 0 0

Helping your child with speech homework will be an important advantage for your child's progress. If your child experiences difficulty or frustration, stop. Try to make your sessions brief and positive.

Thank you for your support. Please sign and return this when you have completed the above lessons.

Additional Teacher Comment *(optional):*

Parent signature _____

Please write any comments, if any, on the back of this memo.

HAPPY HATS B&W FLANNEL BOARD FIGURES

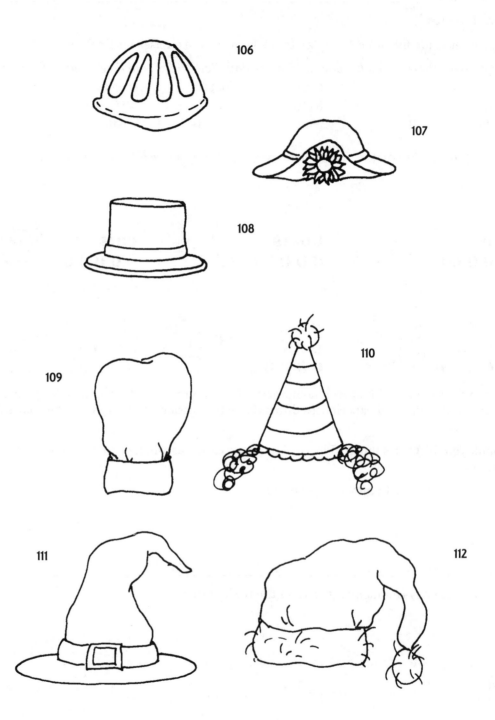

106

107

108

109

110

111

112

354

TEACHER NOTES

TEACHER NOTES

TEACHER NOTES

TEACHER NOTES